The Wendell Castle Book
of Wood Lamination

The Wendell Castle Book
of Wood Lamination

Wendell Castle

David Edman

Photographs by George Kamper

VNR VAN NOSTRAND REINHOLD COMPANY
NEW YORK CINCINNATI TORONTO LONDON MELBOURNE

Printed in the United States of America
Designed by Loudan Enterprises

Published in 1980 by Van Nostrand Reinhold Company
A division of Litton Educational Publishing, Inc.
135 West 50th Street, New York, NY 10020, U.S.A.

Van Nostrand Reinhold Limited
1410 Birchmount Road
Scarborough, Ontario M1P 2E7, Canada

Van Nostrand Reinhold Australia Pty. Ltd.
17 Queen Street
Mitcham, Victoria 3132, Australia

Van Nostrand Reinhold Company Limited
Molly Millars Lane
Wokingham, Berkshire, England

16 15 14 13 12 11 10 9 8 7 6 5 4 3 2 1

Library of Congress Cataloging in Publication Data

Castle, Wendell, 1932—
  Wendell Castle book of wood lamination.

  Includes index.
  1. Furniture making. 2. Laminated wood.
I. Edman, David, joint author. II. Title.
TT194.C37   684.1'043   79-19401
ISBN 0-442-21478-2

Contents

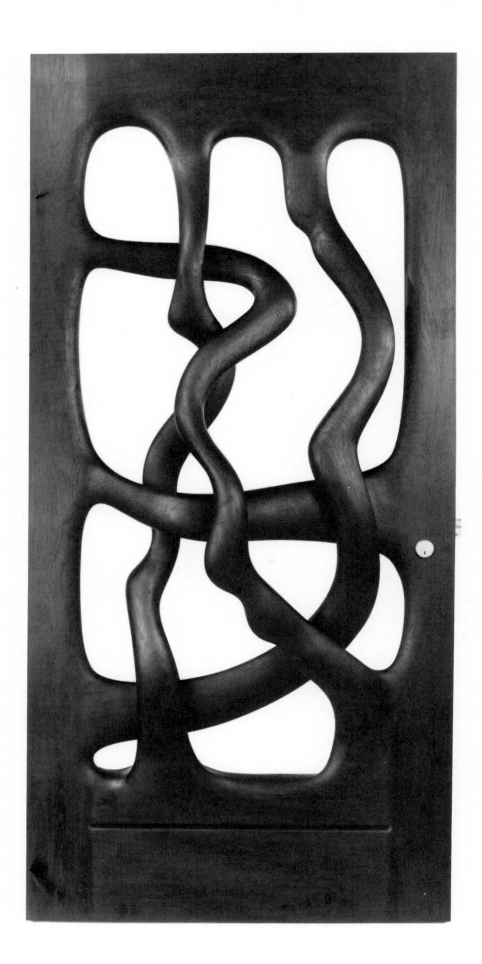

The construction of this door provided me an opportunity to examine artistically the motion and grace of wood in its organic state.

Acknowledgments

I find myself left with the feeling that this volume almost requires yet another to list the many people whose influence and help have played an important part in my work. Since such a list would be manifestly impossible in the allotted space, I limit my acknowledgments to those immediately concerned with this book.

First I would like to thank John Kelsey, editor of *Fine Woodworking,* who originally conceived of a book of this nature and offered to assist with the writing. Then my gratitude to Nancy Newman Green of Van Nostrand Reinhold, who encouraged me to persist with this book when John found it impossible to continue as writing assistant. To David Edman, who took up these duties, and to George Kamper, whose expertise in photography was matched by his patience in the hour upon hour of chronicling the progress of various projects. Also my thanks to Guildford L. Isherwood for certain engineering data. Nor would I forget my studio assistants, Stephen Proctor, Donald Sottile, and Stephen Toms for their help with many of the details.

Finally I am indebted in more ways than I can tell to my wife, Nancy Jurs, a craftsman in her own right, but also spouse, mother, companion, critic, and helper. It is to her that this book is dedicated.

1.

The Craft of Lamination

In the early 1960s a quiet revolution began to take place in the field of woodworking. Simply stated, it involved the gluing together of layers of wood, a process known as *lamination*.

There was nothing new about the technique as such. Lamination in one form or another is almost as old as woodworking itself. In the past, lamination was used as a means of increasing wood bulk. For example, in the Middle Ages wood sculpture was frequently made from rather crudely laminated wood. The process as practiced at that time, however, tended to be unreliable. Glues were temperamental; many were made according to home recipes and could not be counted on to provide a lasting bond. Also, the tools were not precise enough to provide the exact gluing surfaces required for proper laminating. Laminations had to be dowelled or scarfed if they were not to fall apart.

In more recent times, lamination came to be regarded as a means of greatly increasing the tensile strength of wood. It was found that the interruption and restructuring of wood grain through a process of layering and gluing under carefully controlled pressure increased the wood's capacity to withstand fracturing and splitting. In addition, it stabilized the wood against warping to such a degree that laminated wood forms could be utilized in such critical applications as airplane propellers.

It was a combination of these qualities—strength, stability, mass—that began to make its appeal to me in the early 1960s. Strength and stability are always welcome additions to woodworking procedures, for wood in its natural state is only fitfully strong and is notoriously unstable. As for an increase in wood mass, it seemed to me that here lay possibilities for entirely new approaches to wood as a medium of artistic expression.

The importance of these three factors becomes evident when one realizes that wood in its raw state, as lumber, is an exceedingly unreliable material. I am not referring to the matter of knots and imperfections alone. There is something far more basic at issue; namely, the fact that a typical board, if it is to be utilized in traditional furnituremaking, cannot exceed much more than four inches [10.2cm] in thickness. Why? Simply because it is all but impossible to dry adequately wood of greater dimensions. Even if properly cured,

Fig. 1-1. Wooden statuary from the latter half of the twelfth century reveals the lamination procedures of that day (and incidentally the problem of the fracture of wood along the grain). This group is from Erill-la-Vall, Spain. (Photo: Courtesy of Hirmer Fotoarchiv, Munich, Germany)

thicker wood will remain dangerously unstable. This is because the cellular structure of wood is such that its outer surface blots up humidity when the surrounding air is damp, while, under arid conditions, moisture in the wood is released into the air. The result of these phenomena is motion. At its surface, wood expands and contracts relative to its moisture content. This, in turn, causes internal stress, which, in wood of larger dimensions, results in a series of characteristic splits along the grain line.

As a consequence of this limitation, woodworking over the centuries has been forced to deal with thin pieces of wood fashioned in a more or less geometric arrangement. In other words, the wood-splitting factor has confined the craft to a rectilinear aesthetic, leaving the woodworker to deal with his art in the coinage of angles and planes.

Fig. 1-2. Characteristic splitting of a hardwood beam, the result of moisture imbalance. Lamination procedures tend to defeat this phenomenon.

Fig. 1-3. A rococo table, dating from the eighteenth century; its traditional woodworking techniques are concealed under elaborate ornamentation and veneer. (Photo: Courtesy of Christie's)

To be sure, attempts have been made to soften the angular nature of cabinetry. Ornamentation has been superimposed on the cubelike structure to conceal its essentially rectangular construction. Straight lines have been shaped in a manner to give the illusion of curvature. Nevertheless, woodworking has remained essentially within the geometric mode, and this simply because of the effect of moisture upon wood.

Interestingly, its angular nature has been reinforced by another ancient invariable, namely, the linear flow of wood grain. Grain is an inescapably visual aspect of woodcraft. Ordinarily, grain is oriented along the length of the board. But what happens when the woodworker wants to exhibit a curved grain? With traditional techniques such a possibility was severely limited by the demands of structural integrity, leaving woodworkers with only one practical approach to linear grain flow—namely, jointure that was essentially angular in nature.

The possibilities provided by lamination techniques encouraged me to challenge these age-old restrictions upon the woodworking art. By drastically increasing the overall size of the "board" through lamination procedures, by negating the splitting factor through a process that multiplies the stability and strength many times over, I found myself freed from the necessity to operate within the confines of lines and planes. Wood, I realized, could be shaped and formed and carved in ways limited now only by my imagination!

In addition, it became possible to control the flow of the grain. Through lamination procedures, wood grain could be trained, as it were, to change directions at the behest of the woodworker. The form of wood in its living state—trunks, limbs, vines, and so forth—became accessible to artistic reformulation through the eye and hand of human imagination.

Today lamination is widely practiced. It has become increasingly evident that the procedure provides a radically new approach in the field of woodworking. This approach is not necessarily a rival to older techniques; rather, it can be a partner, complementing old techniques while allowing the woodworker to be open to new areas of design. As I have often put the matter to students, lamination has greatly increased the vocabulary of the woodworker. It has provided a versatile new language undreamed of only a few decades ago.

As is true with any new approach, there remains a certain hesitancy on the part of many to experiment with lamination techniques. This may be due in part to ignorance of the procedures involved—a matter this book will attempt to rectify. In addition, there are many who have misgivings about forsaking the old woodworking virtues for a technique that seems brashly modern. There can be no doubt about the hold the old woodworking mystique has on those committed to the craft: the tools, the skills, the tricks, the guild mentality.

After all, woodworking is one of the oldest crafts. Were not many of its subtle techniques known and practiced during the Bronze Age? Was not Jesus of Nazareth numbered among its practitioners? As with other ancient craft disciplines—weaving, metalworking, pottery—one feels the weight of timeless traditions. Surely, adherence to these traditions is laudable but only insofar as it does not stifle expression. There are some—and I am one of them—who feel that the creative imagination must never be inhibited by the past.

There will also be some who suppose the lamination technique is too advanced for any but the most qualified craftsman. The elaborateness of laminated forms seems to imply a range of tools and know-how that is far beyond the skilled amateur. Rather, the reverse is true. The technique tends, in fact, to be quite elementary. Not only the principles of design, but the woodworking procedures themselves can be quickly learned by those with reasonable aptitude. Small pieces especially are within the capabilities of an average high school shop class.

In general, the larger the laminated form, the more exacting and difficult the process. But smaller pieces can be readily conceived and executed by the basement amateur. For example, a small chest or mirror frame can be constructed with the help of only one power tool—a jointer, which will provide the exact gluing surfaces necessary for the process. For the rest, the only tools needed are a coping saw, clamps, chisels, rasps, and sandpaper.

The accessibility of the technique on this scale can be demonstrated by a recent work from my own shop. Not long ago I was approached by the faculty of the Eastman School of Music to make a jewel box as a birthday gift for Shinichi Suzuki, the innovative teacher of violin. I found the idea rather appealing, since it occurred to me that the violin that Suzuki has introduced to so many thousands is itself a kind of jewel box.

Twenty-five years ago construction of a jewel box would doubtless have entailed a framework of members arranged in a geometric manner and joined by one of the traditional means of jointure, such as finger-jointing or dovetailing. The ornamentation of the rectilinear skeleton would likely have been added on instead of having been integral to the structure.

With lamination, however, it was possible for me to synthesize form and design with even so small a piece as a jewel box. This meant that in the design phase I could adopt as my muse a style of organic form that, in this case, reflects the occasional mounding of wood in its natural state.

In order to show the relative ease with which this small article can be constructed using the lamination technique, I have here begun a piece similar to the one presented to Suzuki. It involves a procedure I call *stack lamination*. In this case, six laminae (layers of wood) were required, each approximately 1⅛ inches [2.9cm] thick.

I selected from my wood shed a piece of cherry, a common hardwood that is not only very pleasant to work with, but also possesses the virtue of aging beautifully, taking on a characteristic rich and red hue. I then took the board into my shop, where I measured it and cut the necessary length on the radial-arm saw.

The first step in preparing the rough-sawn lumber involved the jointer, a power tool that not only cleans wood, but also provides the exactly flat surface so necessary for proper gluing. I placed the board upon the jointer with the "cup" side down, then fed the board through the jointer in such a way that the grain followed the direction of the cut. (Most woodworkers are able to tell grain direction at a glance. If for some reason the wood is fed through the jointer in such a way that the knife works against the grain, the "tear-out" problem is heard before it is observed.) In this case, I passed the board across the jointer two or three times until I was left with one perfectly flat side.

Fig. 1-4. *A good selection of hardwoods on hand frees the woodworker from endless visits to the lumber dealer. Here at my studio I am able to select a piece of cherry stock for my jewel box that will serve the requirements of both quality and economy.*

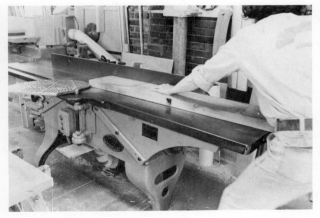

Fig. 1-5. *The jointer both cleans the stock and provides one perfectly flat face.*

I might add here that there is no reason why the purist cannot hand-plane the board. Although it is difficult to match the precision of a power jointer, a piece of this scale does not require the exact tolerances larger laminated works do. In this case, a jointer plane could be run along the grain; if the grain is irregular or curly, the plane would move across the wood diagonally.

With one side jointed, I then ran the board through the power planer, jointed surface down. Again I took care that the knife rotated in the direction of the grain, not against it.

This procedure completed, I was left with two exactly parallel surfaces—the fundamental requirement in the lamination process.

Fig. 1-6. The jointed surface rides across the table of the planer, giving the reverse side not only a flat surface, but one that is exactly parallel to the other—a must in the lamination process.

With board surfaces prepared, I was ready to begin laminating. The process started with laminations #2 and #3 (#1 being the bottom of the box). I traced the design line for both exterior and interior of the box from a top, or "plan," view onto the face of the #2 lamination. In the accompanying photograph (fig. 1-7), note that both laminations have been sawn in half and jointed. This permits band-sawing of the interior line.

Figure 1-8 shows a particular arc being refined by the curve of a sleeve from a spindle sander. This procedure is not meant to assure a perfect curve; rather, it is to make certain that the interior can be accommodated by the spindle sander. In production work it is necessary wherever possible to use available power equipment. Whereas the amateur will be more likely to have the leisure to take several hours sanding an interior surface by hand, the professional may not have more than a few minutes for this task.

Fig. 1-7. The walls of the jewel box are traced from a planned, or top, view. Note that two pieces are involved here, separable for ease of band-sawing.

Fig. 1-8. Refining an interior trace line with a sleeve from a spindle sander will prove a time-saver later along.

I then used the band saw to saw out the interior line on both halves of lamination #2. For those who do not have a band saw, a jig saw or saber saw—or even a coping saw or a bow saw—will serve this purpose just as well.

I next drew together the two halves of lamination #2 and used the joined piece to provide the interior line for lamination #3. It was important that the interior of these two parts turn out exactly the same, for they were to become as one piece. It was also at this point that I traced out the interior line on lamination #4, the first lamina of the lid of the box. This served later as a guide for the area to be gouged out to coincide with the interior shape of the base.

Fig. 1-9. A band saw cuts away the jewel box's interior.

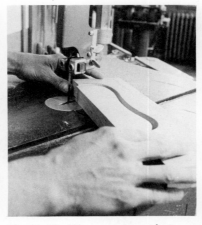

Fig. 1-10. The opposing side is similarly band-sawed.

Fig. 1-11. Tracing the interior line on the lamina that will serve as the lid. This line provides a guide for gouging the portion of the lid to be hollowed.

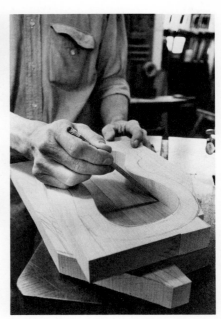

I then edge-glued and clamped laminations #2 and #3. When the glue had set, I prepared the two pieces for face-gluing.

I began the process of face-gluing, as always, with a hand-planing to insure a precise matching of the two glue surfaces. Next, I applied glue, taking care to ensure that the interior walls of the box were lined up as perfectly as possible. I then clamped the two laminae.

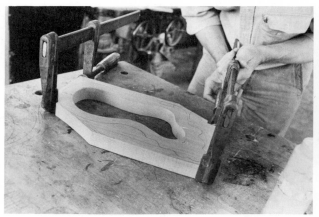

Fig. 1-12. *After band-sawing away the interior, I glue together the two halves.*

Fig. 1-13. *After hand-planing the surface to smooth away irregularities, I face-glue laminations #1 and #2.*

Fig. 1-14. *Close to two tons of pressure are provided by quick-action clamps.*

Fig. 1-15. *When the glue has set, I give the interior a finish sanding with a spindle sander.*

Fig. 1-16. *With interior walls sanded, the bottom is laminated into place.*

Fig. 1-17. *The band saw now excises the exterior wall line of the jewel box.*

Fig. 1-18. *I begin work on the lid by tracing the exterior line of the form onto a board. I have already marked this piece of wood, incidentally, with the interior line.*

After I removed the clamps, I sanded the interior surface on a spindle sander. Although this step may seem premature, viewed in the totality of the operation it becomes evident that this was the only time when the interior sanding could be accomplished with ease. In lamination work, as in any other form of woodworking, a few minutes forethought may result in hours of time saved. Even by hand, this sanding could have been accomplished much more quickly at this point than it could have after the bottom was attached. Here also we see why construction began with laminations #2 and #3.

Sanding completed, I placed the joined laminations #2 and #3 upon the base lamina, then face-glued and clamped them.

When the glue had set, I band-sawed away the exterior shape of the three laminae.

With the rough work on the base complete, I turned my attention to the lid. I traced the exterior line upon lamination #4, then face-glued this lamination to a matching board, lamination #5. A smaller piece, which would eventually serve as sculptural relief, formed the sixth and final lamination. Finally, I band-sawed away the exterior line for the lid.

At that point, the base and lid of the jewel box were complete except for hinging, carving, and finishing.

Fig. 1-15.

Fig. 1-16.

Fig. 1-17.

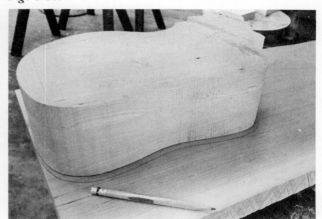

Fig. 1-18.

While it was in this rough state—when clamp marks were of no consequence—I applied the hinges. For a jewel box of this nature, only the best hardware will do. Figure 1-19 shows me in the process of mortising the hinges. The hinges themselves were of cast brass, imported from Scandinavia, and very expensive!

Once the hinges were installed, I began to gouge out the interior of the lid. This not only softened the interior contours, but lightened considerably the weight of the lid.

Fig. 1-19. Application of hardware is not necessarily the last step in furnituremaking. Here I apply the hinges while I can still secure the piece without concern about clamp marks. Also, attaching base and lid enables me to begin to treat the piece as a unified construction.

Fig. 1-20. Hollowing the lid's interior with gouge and mallet, using the line previously traced.

I completed this phase by sanding the excavated portion with a flexible disc sander. Please note the importance here of attaching the sandpaper to the flexible disc by glue, not with a retaining screw and washer.

Figure 1-22 shows the jewel box before it is carved and finished. The lid and base are correctly fitted. Hinges have been installed. The interiors of both base and lid have been finely sanded to the point that only a light touch-up will be required prior to oiling.

I began the work of sculpting by outlining contours with a felt-tipped marker. Woodworkers have available to them a variety of ways of dealing with sculptured form. Some work with models; some depend on fully dimensional drawings. For me, however, the shape of a piece at this stage will be sufficiently clear in my mind that external markings of this nature will do.

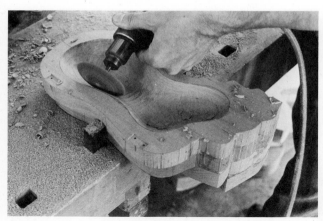

Fig. 1-21. A flexible disc sander smooths away the gouge marks.

Fig. 1-22. The jewel box with most of the interior work completed. Sculpting of the exterior follows.

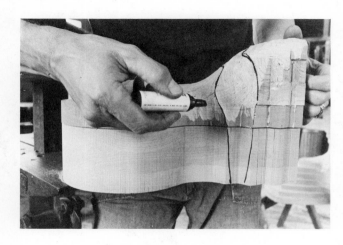

Fig. 1-23. A felt-tipped marker delineates the contours of the sculpture.

The series of photographs that follows (figs. 1–24 through 1–27) shows how the sculpted form emerged and was refined.

Fig. 1-24. The sculpted form begins to emerge with the help of a well-sharpened gouge and mallet.

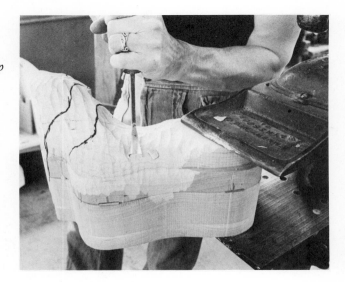

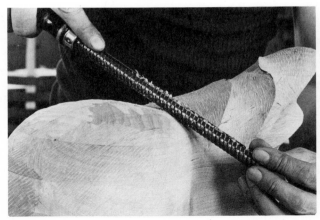

Fig. 1-25. Refinement is provided with a Surform. In the process, I removed the hinges one at a time so that I could shape and sand the surrounding area.

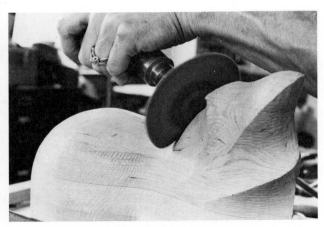

Fig. 1-26. The finishing phase begins with a flexible disc sander, first with a #60 grit, then working up to a #150. Hand-sanding follows, for which I used a #220 grit paper.

Fig. 1-27. I give the jewel box its first coat of boiled linseed oil and turpentine. As a finishing touch, I will later attach a leather bottom and lid stay.

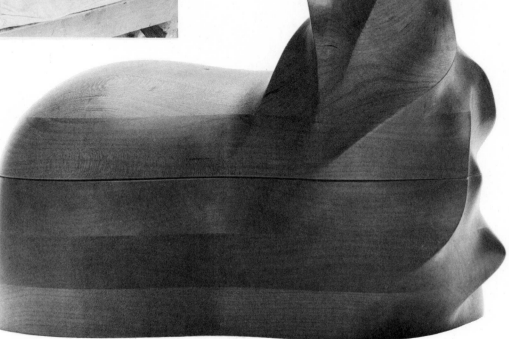

Fig. 1-28.

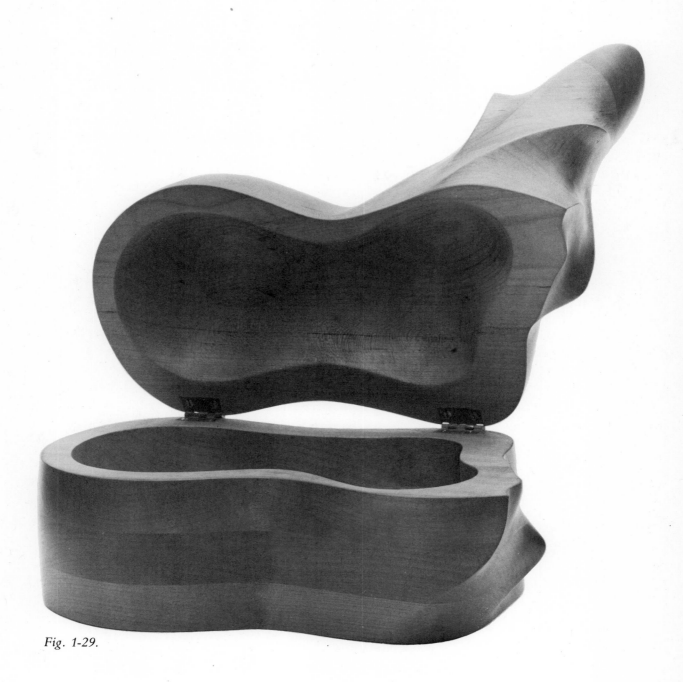

Fig. 1-29.

2.

Lamination: Tools and the Workshop

The manner in which a woodworker equips and arranges his shop is intensely personal and reflective of his basic outlook and values. There are, of course, a great number of books on the market to inform the amateur and the novice on how to set up a shop. Such books come with a great many facts and figures aimed at arranging an ideal workshop. The problem, however, for the woodworker who wishes to deal in large laminated forms—and make a living at it—is that he can never hope to own an *ideal* workshop. Why? Simply because it's too expensive. Unless one has managed to inherit a fortune from a rich aunt, it is not likely that he will possess so much as an ideal work space, not to mention the kind of power and hand equipment he might like to own.

The realities are more likely to be as follows. First, our craftsman will find himself located in a cheaply rented building that was originally intended for some other purpose. Second, his workshop will be outfitted with used equipment, which he has located by chance or by luck and has purchased on credit.

Accordingly, a chapter on tools and the workshop as it applies to this type of situation will make more sense if based on the experiences of someone who is no stranger to the situation just described. What follows, then, arises from my own experience. Because of that, my descriptions may seem opinionated.

What is more, they are delivered by one who claims no expertise in tool analysis. For all that, the truth is that twenty years ago, when my work with sculpture began to branch out into the area of furniture design, I owned little more than a set of hand tools. My music rack, described in Chapter 5, was made primarily with power equipment owned by the School for American Craftsmen.

Using machinery that belongs to other people is not, needless to say, a practice woodworkers care to tolerate forever. So when, in 1963, I received a substantial commission to furnish executive offices for a local industrial firm, I invested the funds in the beginnings of a workshop. First I rented an old stable in Rochester's Third Ward, then I began the process of locating good power tools—used.

That process has continued to this day. I spend a considerable portion of my spare time searching out good buys in woodworking equipment, and with it the continual upgrading of my shop. It is out of these experiences that I offer my reflections on the type of environment and equipment that best lends itself to the laminating task. These comments should not be construed as a step-by-step manual on how to set up a woodworker's shop. Nor are they addressed to the amateur who will be constructing smaller pieces and hence will not require the kind of precision machinery I describe.

Let me begin by noting that I currently occupy my third workshop.* This one is located in an abandoned railroad station in the village of Scottsville, New York, about ten miles south of Rochester. Three full-time assistants are employed in the shop, as well as a number of part-time helpers.

In the tradition of American railroad stations, the structure we occupy is large and sturdily built. Its windows are oversize, supplying us with an abundance of natural light. I would not call it an ideal workshop, but it does provide a pleasant sort of ambience for the work we do; and I would like at least to think that in essentials it does not differ markedly from woodshops of other lands—and other centuries too.

Fig. 2-1. The old Baltimore and Ohio station in Scottsville, New York, which serves as Wendell Castle's woodworking studio.

*Actually, I am in my *fourth* workshop now. Since writing this book I have moved my shop to renovated quarters in an adjacent bean mill with almost three times the floor space as the third workshop had. There are currently five assistants.

In her novel *Adam Bede,* George Eliot describes the woodshop of Jonathan Burge as it appeared on the afternoon of 18 June 1799. Like ours, it had about it the scent of wood, the sound of saws and mallets, the give-and-take of workshop banter. ". . . the slanting sunbeams shone through transparent shavings that flew before the steady plane, and lit up the fine grain of oak paneling which stood propped against the wall." A major difference between the workshop of Jonathan Burge and mine would no doubt be the presence of power tools in our Scottsville railroad station. Here the general calm is occasionally broken by the shriek of the radial-arm saw, the thump of the oscillating sander, the whine of the power plane. Still, it is a woodworker's shop in the old tradition, even if its products challenge certain traditions and build upon yet others. Out of its evolution permit me, then, some general commentary on the following: the workshop, power tools, hand tools and accessories, hand power tools, wood, adhesives and finishing materials, and safety.

Fig. 2-2. A summer afternoon in the benchroom of Castle's workshop.

THE WORKSHOP

As regards a site for a workshop, I have always felt that access should be a dominant consideration. A good workshop should allow for the easy entry and removal of machinery, wood, projects, and the like. This does not necessarily mean an array of loading docks, but it does call into question the prevailing tendency to place workshops in basements.

The room itself should be large enough to provide ample clearance around workbenches and power machinery. The woodworker who plans to move into a new shop of marginal proportions should draw a floor plan to scale and then, with colored pieces of cardboard representing machinery and also cut to scale, work through problems of interference and work flow until they are fully solved.

A desirable feature for any workshop is a high ceiling—lumber can become extremely awkward when ceilings are low. Oversize or double doors also can make life much easier. Floors should be sufficiently sturdy to support machinery without vibrating.

Electrical service to the building should be ample, with wiring reasonably up to date. A circuit breaker panel is preferable to a fuse box, and fuses preferable to pennies. Also, there is definite advantage in having three-phase electrical power within the building. If such proves not to be the case—and it may not if you are located in a residential area—inquire about the cost of bringing it in.

Lighting is another major consideration. An abundance of natural light is always desirable provided it does not entail excessive heat loss in the winter. As for artificial light, fluorescent is better than incandescent, in that it provides a softer, more regular light and tends to ease shadows. Regardless of its source, good light is an absolute necessity for both efficiency and safety.

Heat is another important factor if you plan to engage in serious lamination projects. Many woodshops can function perfectly well with wood stoves that are stoked first thing in the morning and allowed to die down at night. The considerable temperature swing that results during any given twenty-four-hour period may be acceptable for more traditional woodworking, but will not do at all for laminating. On the contrary, the lamination process requires a controlled, even heat twenty-four hours a day. The critical factor here is not temperature, but humidity, although they are, of course, interrelated, and that is where the problem lies. Fluctuations in shop temperature are accompanied by fluctuations in the moisture content of wood laminae. And that can prove disastrous. To prevent this, I keep my workshop at a uniform 62°F [16.6°C] during the winter—day and night. At the same time, a humidifier puts about ten gallons [38 l] of water per day into the air to keep the hygrometer at about 40 percent.

With regard to the general state of any workshop, I would recommend two auxiliary systems for consideration by the serious woodworker. The first is a centralized vacuum system, connected individually to the various power machines to help remove sawdust and chips. Such a system provides an environment far more conducive to creative woodworking than does a continual shroud of wood dust. The second adjunct to a well-run shop is a compressed air system. Compressed air may be utilized for all sorts of tasks, most notably for air-driven tools, which in my estimation cannot be surpassed for quietness, efficiency, and safety.

In my shop, compressed air is conveyed to various take-offs by iron gas pipe. Pressure is maintained at 105–110 psi. Needless to say, the important factor is not so much the pressure as the volume. Air-driven tools require anywhere from 5–25 CFM; this means that if several tools are in use at any one time, a minimum of 50 CFM might be needed. This, in turn, indicates a compressor requirement in the 10–15 hp range.

All air compressors must have moisture traps to collect water and filters to remove particles. Some air-driven machines require automatic oilers in the line to lubricate moving parts. Regulators at various take-offs can provide an adjustable pressure.

POWER MACHINERY

Before dealing with specific power tools used in the lamination craft, I would like to make some general comments about purchasing power tools.

First, the serious woodworker should think twice before purchasing equipment offered by large chain retailers. Although some of these tools may be better than others, the best of them will not in all likelihood provide the precision required for good and lasting laminations in larger pieces. If you are inclined to buy such machinery in any event, don't be seduced by terms like *heavy duty* or *industrial rated*. These, I think, are more the invention of admen than anything else. The term *horsepower* also can be misleading. It can be measured in a variety of ways—brake, free running, loaded, and so forth. The knowledgeable buyer of tools, therefore, pays more attention to amperage than to the stated horsepower.

The best power machinery is the type used in cabinet and furniture factories. Not only are these machines designed to operate at critical tolerances, but they are constructed so sturdily and expertly that their age is relatively unimportant. Good power saws and planers can be thirty years old and more and still function superbly; their value may actually increase as time goes on.

As I have already noted, the average craftsman will not have enough money to purchase such equipment new. Rather, he must seek out used machinery from three sources: individual owners, tool dealers, auctions. Whatever the source, the buyer must be extremely cautious when purchasing used tools. It is of considerable importance, for example, to be sure that parts for some purportedly good buy remain available, that the machine under consideration has not already joined the ranks of the obsolete.

A few words about electricity. I wish someone had told me what I am about to write, because I once let an unusually fine variety saw get away from me simply because it was a three-phase tool and at the time I was unaware of what that meant and how easy it was to adapt three-phase machinery to ordinary workshop conditions.

Just what *is* three-phase electricity? In laymen's terms, it is a type of power supplied by the utility company at either 208 volts or 220 volts (or, in rare instances, even higher voltage) by means of a series of three hot wires that provide a staggered sequence of electrical impulses, thereby permitting a motor to achieve full torque more quickly and to run more efficiently at a lower amperage than is possible with single-phase power. Most three-phase motors may be adjusted to the voltage provided by switching hot wires.

Three-phase motors are preferable to their single-phase equivalents. They are cheaper to buy, cheaper to run, less likely to break down. Also, they produce more torque power than the same motor constructed for single-phase operation.

To be sure, the problem for some woodworkers will be that three-phase power is not available in their area. If this proves to be so in your case, be advised that you can buy motorized phase converters or increasingly inexpensive transistorized phase converters.

The point has not so much to do with the vagaries of electricity as with the fact that many of the superb power machines that might recommend themselves to a woodworker will come in the three-phase mode, and the would-be buyer should not be put off by it.

Moisture Meter

For lamination, a moisture meter is an indispensable tool for, in effect, it indicates the compatibility of one piece of wood with another. It operates on the principle of resistance: The more moisture there is in wood, the less resistance to the flow of electricity. A probe is driven into the wood and the degree of moisture present is calibrated electronically.

Fig. 2-3. Determining moisture levels in wood is an absolutely essential procedure in the lamination process. A surplus air force moisture meter, possibly used for testing laminated aircraft parts such as propellers, serves the purpose admirably in our workshop.

A variety of such meters is available on the market. The more expensive models tend to take in the entire range of wood moisture conditions. Such versatility is rarely needed in the lamination workshop. A meter that calibrates levels in the air-dried/kiln-dried ranges will be cheaper and serve just as well.

My own meter, incidentally, is an old air force surplus affair for which I paid pennies. The penalty here was an odd battery size, but the problem will be overcome shortly when the unit is converted to 110 volts.

Radial-Arm Saw

Ordinarily the radial-arm saw is used for rough sawing. Timbers taken from the wood pile can easily be laid on the saw's table and there cut to convenient lengths.

The radial-arm saw is not—and indeed cannot be—the kind of precision tool the variety saw is. Even the best radial-arm saw will wiggle a thousandth of an inch here and there as it travels up and down its track. For this reason, this particular power tool does not have the importance in lamination procedures that other saws have, and the woodworker need not spend a great deal of money on it.

Fig. 2-4. Radial-arm saw. Given the exacting requirements of lamination work, in which variations in the range of thousandths of an inch can be critical, a radial-arm saw is primarily a roughing tool.

Variety Saw

The variety saw goes by a number of names: *bench saw, table saw, circular saw,* and so forth. In terms of precision cutting, it is the most important tool in the shop. When in the market for a variety saw, the wise lamination woodworker will not spare expense.

The size of variety saw is indicated both by blade diameter and motor horsepower. For serious woodworkers, the preferred blade size will tend toward the large end of the available spectrum—closer to sixteen inches [40cm] than to ten [25.4cm]. Horsepower in variety saws begins at around 1, but don't be satisfied with a machine until you find yourself in the neighborhood of 5 hp.

Fig. 2-5. Variety saw. Also called a table saw, circular saw, bench saw, this is a Tannowitz sixteen-inch [40.6cm] model with a rack-and-pinion fence.

A tilting arbor is an all-but-universal feature of variety saws these days. If you come across an old-fashioned tilting table type for sale be aware of the difficulties posed by this particular application.

For lamination work it is important that variety saws have rip fences and cross-cut guides that provide exceedingly precise cuts. The type of fence that rides along two tracks will not offer the precision provided by the rack-and-pinion type. Once fitted into its tapered holes, a rack-and-pinion fence offers a perfect edge for guiding wood through the blade. As for cross-cut guides, the best type fits into a dovetailed way (or slot).

When buying a second-hand variety saw, the woodworker should determine if the blade is belt-driven or powered directly by the motor. The advantage of the latter is a more vibration-free operation. Once again, this is a distinct advantage for lamination work.

Variety saws are available in exceedingly elaborate models. Some offer a split table, with half sliding on rollers to guide the board along. Others come equipped with a "scoring blade" to prevent chip-out. Yet others have hydraulic lift capabilities and the like. Such options quickly push up the price on the used market, yet may not prove all that useful. Rather than looking for options, be concerned about the condition of the basic components—motor, bearings, guides, and so forth. Some names to keep in mind are Oliver, Northfield, and Tannowitz.

As for blades, I prefer the carbide-tipped combination blade. Mine is left on the machine for all cutting and removed only when the blade needs sharpening or when some special cut may be required with a dado blade or the like. With regular shop use, the blade should be given a professional sharpening three times per year.

Band Saw

The band saw is used constantly in lamination work. Ours will be switched on and off dozens of times a day as we cut laminae to various shapes. Because it serves as something of a workhorse, I would recommend that the lamination-oriented woodworker be prepared to spend a little extra here.

Fig. 2-6. Band saw. The most frequently used power tool in our workshop.

Band saws are classed by throat size, the distance from the blade to the support column. The smallest size band saw—twelve inches [30.5cm] or there-abouts—will likely prove too insubstantial for most lamination work; forty inches [101.6cm], on the other hand, seems excessive. Look for a band saw with a minimum of twenty inches [50.8cm], and see how much larger you can go before your bankroll suffers total depletion.

When shopping for a band saw, make sure the wheels and guides are in good condition. If the machine you are inspecting can be switched on, see that the blade runs straight and true. Feel for vibrations, which indicate the presence of worn bearings. This problem can ordinarily be felt long before it can be heard. In larger band saws, keep your eye out for a Tannowitz, Oliver, or Northfield. Good band saws in smaller dimensions are made by Rockwell and Powermatic.

Jointer

When inspecting a used jointer, do not wait long before inspecting the cutter head. If you find an old-fashioned square head, and if you value safety, let the machine go. If you find a round head, but only two knives, you have come upon an old roughing jointer and, because of the more pronounced mill marks left by this type of jointer, you will not be guaranteed the kind of surface required for good and lasting glue joints. But if you find a round cutter head with three—or better, *four*—knives, begin to look at the machine as a prospective buy.

Jointers vary in blade length from about four to thirty-six inches [10.2–91.4cm]. The woodworker interested in laminating should set his sights on a jointer with a blade in the neighborhood of sixteen inches [40.6cm]. Beyond the cutter head problems mentioned above, age has little bearing on the quality of jointers. I have seen a sixty-year-old model that worked beautifully. One of my former machines was more than thirty years old and, aside from the excessive care required by its Babbitt bearings, it gave me excellent service. There was nothing wrong with the Babbitt bearings, as such. They just needed daily oilings and constant adjustment of V belts to insure that they did not wear unevenly. With such attention they gave me more than ten years' use.

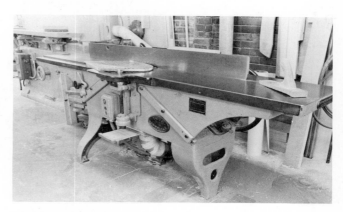

Fig. 2-7. Jointer. Since lamination procedures require face-jointing as well as edge-jointing, the jointer in a lamination shop must possess adequate width capacities. Shown here is a Yates-American with a sixteen-inch [40.6cm] head.

When looking at a used jointer, keep the names Yates-American, Northfield, Oliver, and Porter in mind. Also, since precision setting of the knives as well as the infeed and outfeed tables is critical, make sure that the instruments of adjustment are in good repair.

Power Planer

The widths of single-surface power planers run from about twelve to forty-eight inches [30.5– 121.9cm]. For the woodworker regularly engaged in lamination procedures, a twenty-inch [50.8cm] planer is a nice size to own.

In looking at used planers, pay attention to the cutter head. With planers as with jointers, avoid old-fashioned square cutter heads; regular planer heads should possess a minimum of three knives, with four preferred. If you can find a planer with spring-loaded knife lifters, good! This type is easier to adjust. Even better are power planers with built-in knife sharpeners; a sharpener of this sort provides accurate edges and alignment. Whenever knives are removed for sharpening, they must be reinserted with utmost precision, aided always by a dial indicator. Hence the value of spring-loaded lifters or an integral sharpening system. Bed rollers, too, must be adjusted to tolerances measured in the thousandths of inches.

Fig. 2-8. Power planer. The older of two power planers in my studio, this one is a Yates-American with a thirty-inch [76.2cm] capacity.

One desirable feature to look for in used power planers is a segmented infeed roller, which permits several rough boards of varying thicknesses to be fed through the planer at the same time. Although thickness may vary, the planer automatically adjusts to each. Incidentally, the power feed on the planer should be set at the slowest possible rate and left there. A speed of less than twenty feet [6m] per minute leaves nearly indistinguishable mill marks, all of them spaced very closely together. This, in turn, provides the best gluing surface possible.

I might add that new and very expensive power planers come with segmented teeth cutter heads rather than knives. Whereas the efficiency of such blades remains about the same, they do have the virtue of being exceedingly quiet. Also, one tooth chipped on a knot can be replaced individually—a far easier task than trying to salvage a badly nicked knife.

When browsing through the used-planer market, be on the lookout for names like Yates-American, Invincible, Oliver, Buss, Whitney. There are many other fine power planers, no doubt, but these are the ones that occur to me at the moment.

Sanders

Sanders come in all shapes and sizes. Moreover, they are made to function in all kinds of positions. Some sand horizontally, some vertically; some operate from beneath the board being smoothed, some operate on top. In the process, some rotate, some move belt fashion, some oscillate, some utilize a combination of actions. To give a detailed account of all the sanders available on the market would take the better part of a book.

My abbreviated advice to the woodworker in the market for sanding equipment is to secure first the general-purpose machinery—drum, belt, and disc sanders. (A good oscillating belt sander I find invaluable.) Once these are installed and operating, begin to look around for more specialized equipment, such as a spindle sander.

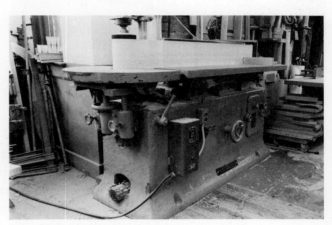

Fig. 2-9. Belt sander. A thirty-year-old Yates-American eight-inch [20.3cm] oscillating belt sander. The oscillating feature is designed to make the belt wear evenly. This particular machine will sand to extremely accurate tolerances.

And So Forth. . . .

There are many other machines not directly related to laminating procedures that nevertheless have their place in a well-equipped workshop: drill presses, jig saws, lathes, milling machines, shapers, mortising machines, and so forth. Although these fall outside the scope of this book, I hope the information above will serve as helpful guidelines in the procurement of any other power machines you might want to own.

HAND TOOLS AND ACCESSORIES
Workbenches, Worktables, and Vises

Because laminated forms tend to assume flowing, asymmetrical shapes, the workbench takes on a special importance for this type of work. These auxiliary devices should be engineered in such a way that they can quickly and surely secure an infinite variety of shapes.

In general, the German and Scandinavian workbenches fulfill this requirement far better than does the typical American worktable. The vises built into the imported workbenches are not only capacious, but versatile. Bench pins inserted at various points along the surface of the bench work with the vises to provide an infinity of holding positions.

For such a workbench, be prepared to pay a premium price—in the neighborhood of $500, and going higher every day! Alas, the alternative is so much poorer, so incomparably more frustrating that the price is more than worth it.

Fig. 2-10. Scandinavian cabinetmaker's bench. I find the bench pin arrangement, in combination with wooden screw vises, particularly useful. The bench top is made of beech; the legs are fir.

If American worktables leave a great deal to be desired, nevertheless there came from this country a vise that is the Cadillac of the line. I refer to the Emmert patternmaker's vise, an ingeniously designed affair that will do everything a vise needs to do, and then some. It is a pity these vises are no longer manufactured—the victims, no doubt, of their high initial cost. They may still be found on the used market, however, and should you happen on one for sale, snap it up immediately!

Whether you have a workbench or worktable, you will occasionally require the use of a "hold-down" for securing a sculpted form to the table. This device has a screw mechanism that attaches to holes in the table and exerts a downward pressure from above upon the form being carved.

Fig. 2-11. Emmert patternmaker's vise. This versatile tool has an unusually large jaw capacity. Moreover, the jaws swivel, tilt, and adjust out of parallel and in two directions.

Fig. 2-12. A typical "hold-down" secures an unsteady piece of sculpture to the work bench.

Clamps

Clamps are the *sine qua non* of lamination work. One hears of all sorts of substitute means for applying pressure to glued laminae—rocks, water under pressure, automobiles driven onto the layers, and so on. Please believe me when I say that nothing short of a fifty-ton [45t] hydraulic press can take the place of a great many clamps properly applied.

Consider the physics of the thing. A small piece of laminated bentwood may require twenty medium-sized clamps spaced on three-inch [7.6cm] centers. Each of these clamps will exert 500 pounds [266.8kg] of pressure, which is to say, the laminated piece is subjected overall to five tons of pressure—and this on a highly concentrated and evenly dispersed basis! Don't try to save money in this area, or you will soon learn what delamination is all about.

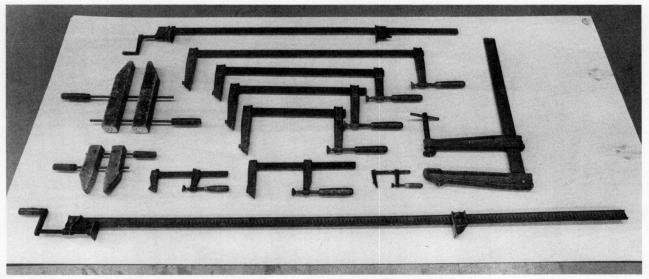

Fig. 2-13. Two wooden hand-screw clamps and three bar clamps frame an assortment of quick-action clamps, the most commonly used in lamination work.

For most laminating procedures I use a quick-action type clamp; that is, a clamp whose adjustable jaw rides up and down a bar and can be locked into place under pressure. The sizes of these clamps range from one that fits into the palm of a hand to those that can barely be lifted by one person. These giant size clamps tend to be custom-made. The bar can be of any height, the reach (or throat) of any depth.

For my own use I prefer wooden handled clamps to all others, mainly because they can be turned easily in a confined space. I would not recommend any particular brands, save only to confess that I have been quite satisfied with the Wetzler clamp.

C-clamps, especially the smaller sized ones, will be used from time to time in lamination work. Larger C-clamps "give" too much to suit me. And whatever the size, C-clamps generally require an inordinate turning of handles, which can be wearisome.

Hand-screw clamps, with their wooden jaws, are good to have around the shop. These are especially useful for clamping nonparallel surfaces or in situations where reach is restricted.

Pipe or bar clamps were designed for clamping panels. Only occasionally will they be used in laminating, but those occasions make these clamps worth owning.

A veneer press is a type of clamp, too. It may come powered by hand screws, or by mechanical or hydraulic mechanisms. In general, a veneer press is a luxury item, but the canny craftsman who happens to run across a used one for very little money will soon count his blessings.

Planes

The hand planes used most often in laminating work are the jointer plane and the jack plane. These are long tools used for smoothing large surfaces. In laminating they are run over the top of each lamina after it has been glued to insure a perfect flatness for the next layer.

Other planes are occasionally employed in the carving stages—smooth planes, block planes, rabbet planes, compass planes, molding planes, as well as their cousins the spokeshaves, drawknives, and scrapers.

Fig. 2-14. Hand planes. Assembled for this photograph are some of the hand planes used in my shop. Left to right: low-angle block plane, block plane, rabbet plane, curved-bottom molding plane, compass plane, smooth plane, scrub plane, jack plane, large jack plane, jointer plane. Foreground: spokeshave, bull-nosed rabbet plane.

The novice woodworker will have some difficulty, I fear, equipping himself with quality hand planes. Neither American nor foreign toolmakers provide anymore the kind of superb instruments that were as nice to look at as they were to use. If this weren't bad enough, the variety of planes available on the market has been curtailed.

What advice can I give to the apprentice who cannot find for himself anything but an ill-forged, ill-adjustable modern plane with a plastic handle? I would not advise going back to a wooden plane, not even the sort one might make for oneself. Wooden planes may look impressive, but that's about the sum of it. No, keep your eye out for an old Stanley. These may be found every now and again, and will provide an unmatched standard of excellence.

Hand Saws

Hand saws are not of much importance to the laminating process. The pleasant image of a wood craftsman armed with a dovetail saw, cutting joints with all of the finesse of a surgeon notwithstanding, the fact is that there simply is no way that hand saws can provide the precision of mechanized equipment. As a result, they are not used often in a lamination workshop. All the same, there will be occasions when hand saws are a convenience. For this reason, the well-equipped workshop should have its share of rip and cross-cut saws, not forgetting back saws and miter saws, dovetail saws and bow saws, veneer saws, keyhole saws, and jig saws. Other saws—offset saws and the like—will gradually join the ranks, purchased for some particular task, then stored on tool board or in drawer, there to await some future service.

Fig. 2-15. Handsaws. Left to right: coping saw, dovetail saw, offset dovetail saw (right-handed), back saw, offset dovetail saw (left-handed), crosscut saw; (in background) veneer saw, Japanese dovetail saw; (being held) Danish frame saw.

Chisels and Gouges

A full set of chisels and gouges will, of course, be maintained in any woodworking shop worthy of the name. A standard set of chisels runs from ⅛ to 1½ inches [.3–3.8cm]. Gouges are numbered according to the degree of their arc, 0 indicating a flat gouge, and progressing from there toward increasingly tight radii. There are no universal standards for the curvature of gouges. Each manufacturer tends to set his own.

Fig. 2-16. Chisels. The left-hand group consists of carving gouges; at the center of the photograph are flat chisels; on the right can be seen specialty carving gouges; and in the foreground is a Japanese paring chisel.

In addition to the more common chisels and gouges, there are any number of special-purpose tools, among them the fishtail gouge, the spoon, the long bend, the back bend, and the paring chisel.

American manufacturers seem to dominate the chisel market, whereas gouges tend to be the domain of foreign toolmakers. In both cases, the use of wooden handles has gradually given way to plastic, which has little bearing on the excellence of the tool, perhaps, but does present certain aesthetic drawbacks.

For driving chisels and gouges, I prefer the round wooden sculptor's mallet to any other hammering device.

Measuring and Marking Tools

To list such tools may seem an exercise in the obvious. Still there are points to be made. A high-quality metal straightedge rule, twenty to thirty-six inches [50.8–91.4cm], is needed first of all. It will be used not only for measuring, but more often still for checking flatness, a crucial element in the lamination process.

A good selection of squares will prove invaluable. A framing square, first of all, is needed to insure straight edges and true ninety-degree angles. Also in this particular arsenal will be a try square, a combination square, and an all-metal precision, or engineer's, square.

A T-bevel will be essential for transferring odd angles.

Marking gauges for determining and scoring depths are necessary for the more mechanical aspects of laminated forms, such as the setting of hinges.

Compass, dividers, steel tapes, levels, snap lines—these and many other such devices will find a useful place in any woodworking shop.

A few words here on the metric system. While I have no doubt of the relative ease of the metric system, or its inevitable adoption in the United

Fig. 2-17. Marking tools. Left to right: folding rule, two sliding T-bevels, calipers, combination square, two marking gauges, tape, combination square. In background: twenty-four-inch [61cm] steel ruler.

States, I remain bound to the older system of measuring in inches and feet and subdividing further into eighths, sixteenths, thirty-seconds, sixty-fourths, and so on. This is partly as a habit of twenty years and more, but it is also the result of purchasing machinery set to the old scale. It would seem that the coming generation of woodworkers will have to be proficient in both systems, to achieve a mental ambidexterity, as it were, until our present system has gone the way of rods and chains, pecks and firkins. To this end, and for the benefit of readers whose primary orientation is the metric system, metric equivalents for various dimensions are indicated in brackets. In many cases, this is largely to give a notion of the range in which we are speaking. For example, a sixty-one-centimeter rule is hardly standard-issue equipment, whereas a twenty-four-inch rule (its equivalent) is.

Rasps, Files, Rifflers, Surforms

Rasps come in a wide variety of lengths, shapes, and textures. The blade may be flat, half-round, or completely round (rattail). The heavy-toothed version is referred to simply as a *coarse rasp;* its less-coarse equivalent is called a *cabinet rasp.*

Fig. 2-18. Rasps. Pictured here is an assortment of wood-forming hand tools known as rasps. On the left are various rifflers; in center foreground may be seen instances of the Stanley Surform along with more traditional rasps; on the right are rattail rasps.

As the teeth grow finer, the implement ceases being a rasp at all and becomes a file. The varieties of files are even more diverse, branching out into, among other things, rifflers, which are specialized files of Italian origin, available from sculptors' supply sources.

There is also on the market today an improved rasp developed by the Stanley Corporation called the Surform. It is perhaps the only hand tool of any consequence developed in the last fifty years. For rough shaping it is almost unsurpassed in its ability to provide a rapid yet controlled rasping. I heartily recommend it to all woodworkers.

POWER HAND TOOLS

The nature of wood lamination work is such that the initial carving stages require fast and efficient removal of large quantities of wood. There is no reason to proceed otherwise. To remove lamination "steps" gently with a rasp or to slowly plane away the "ears" used as clamping points makes no sense whatever. These areas should be taken down to their approximate sculpted form as quickly as possible.

Electric Chain Saws

Of the two hand power tools invaluable for this purpose, the electric chain saw and the power planer, the first must be regarded as the basic roughing implement. The idea of a wood sculptor carving with a tool designed for felling trees and sawing logs may seem rather like a stone sculptor using a jackhammer. For all that, the electric chain saw, properly mastered, can carve with extraordinary facility.

As to recommendations, let me begin by saying that mine is a well-worn, fourteen-inch [35.6cm] Milwaukee. It is an excellent tool, but rather heavy. Other woodworkers might be satisfied with something lighter and cheaper, which can be replaced at little cost as the situation demands.

Power Planers

The power planer also will not be used by the lamination craftsman in the manner intended by the manufacturer. As packaged and sold, the planer is a carpenter's tool that, in effect, serves as a portable jointer. With laminated forms, however, the power planer becomes a carving tool, taking up where the electric chain saw leaves off, rough-removing up to an eighth-inch thickness of wood with every three-inch [7.6cm] pass.

Here again I make no recommendations as to brand, save only to relate that I own a Skil and, after fifteen years of rugged service, it is still going strong.

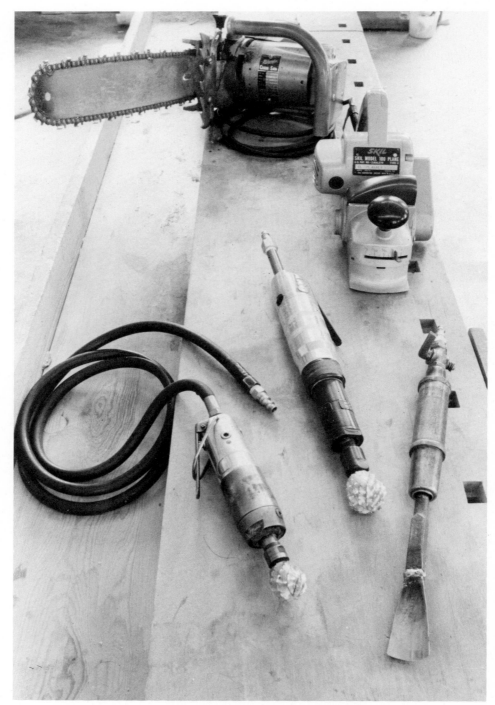

Fig. 2-19. Carving tools. Rough-carving implements shown here include two pneumatic ball mills, pneumatic power chisel, electric hand planer, and an electric chain saw.

Saber Saws

In lamination work, the saber saw functions as an important substitute for the band saw, cutting large areas too heavy or too cumbersome to be accommodated by the band saw. I own two saber saws, one a Bosch air-driven model, the other a Sears Craftsman.

Routers

My experience indicates that it is good to have two routers on hand: the first of these a small laminate trimming router, light and maneuverable; the other a larger router with both a quarter-inch and a half-inch [6.4mm, 12.7mm] collet for larger cutting and grooving.

A word of warning about the router: Many a beginning woodworker will be tempted to use a heavy-duty router for carving, going even so far as to adapt it for use with a ball mill. I would strongly advise against this procedure for reasons of safety. To begin with, a router is not designed for quick on-off operation. Also, its motor is too powerful for this application. If the cutting head catches or jerks, the first problem will be getting the machine turned off; the second will be momentum. In either case there exists the potential for serious damage to the woodworker, not to mention his tool or his project. Routers are important to lamination work, but only when properly used.

Ball Mills

The indispensable tool for carving wood is the ball mill. In essence this tool is nothing more than a ball-shaped, spinning rasp. It was intended originally for metalwork, but now is increasingly used in wood sculpture.

The ball mill comes from the manufacturer custom-made to the woodworker's specifications of size, shape, and number of teeth per inch. The ball mill I ordinarily use has four to five teeth to the inch [2.5cm], with about twice the tooth size used for grinding metal dies and the like.

Ball mills can be powered by electric die grinders, a far safer source of power than the router, not only because of its smaller motor, but also because of the way it is held in the hand. Die grinders will rotate the ball in the 20,000–25,000 rpm range, and develop up to 1 hp. Better still is the air-driven version, which has the advantage of being relatively silent and can be operated with a much greater economy of motion and pressure.

Hand Power Sanders

I would begin by describing my disc sanders, of which I own three—all air-driven. These are in reality body grinders used in automobile repair work. Of the three, the largest develops around 4,000 rpm, the other two 3,000 and 2,000 rpm respectively. All come with a variety of rubber sanding pads to which sandpaper is glued. For rough sanding, nothing can match the efficiency of a body grinder.

Other disc sanders tend to be of the type that can be fitted to a quarter-inch [6.4mm] drill. Disc pads for these come in one-inch increments, beginning at a diameter of one inch and proceeding to five inches [2.5–12.7cm]. The drill will operate these disc sanders at speeds from 2,000 to 2,500 rpm; they can be either electrically powered or air-driven.

As to hand belt sanders, I'm sorry to report that the flexible belt sander made by Rockwell, which I've found quite indispensable in contour-sanding, is no longer being made—the victim, it would seem, of engineering difficulties. I can only hope that Rockwell or some other manufacturer will soon come up with a more reliable version of this tool.

Other power sanders for hand use include vibrating and oscillating pad sanders, either electrically or air-driven. These will doubtless already be found in any woodworker's shop.

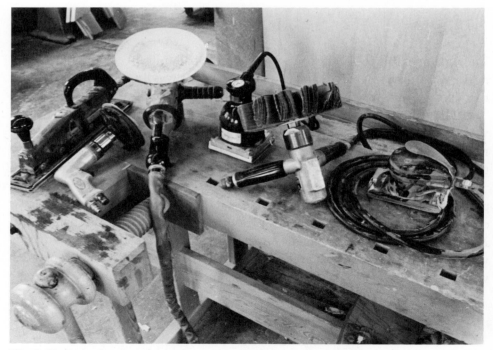

Fig. 2-20. Power hand sanders. A mere fraction of the power sanders available to the workers in our shop can be seen in this photograph. Left to right: oscillating sander, disc-on-air-drill sander, body grinder, electric orbital sander, flap-wheel sander, air orbital sander ("jitterbug").

MATERIALS
Wood

Hardwood is sold as rough timber, in random lengths and widths. The grading system is uniform throughout the United States, but relatively complex all the same. In order to adequately decipher the system, you will need a copy of a pamphlet entitled *Rules for the Measurement and Inspection of Hardwood and Cypress Lumber* issued by the National Hardwood Lumber Association. It costs $2.00 and may be obtained by writing to the association at P.O. Box 34518, Memphis, TN 38134.

The best grade of hardwood is labeled F.A.S., which stands simply for "firsts and seconds." Under this grade come #1 common and #2 common. These lesser grades, incidentally, should not be overlooked by the woodworker, for there are many occasions when wood sawn from between imperfections will serve perfectly well.

Wood is purchased by the board foot, which is a hypothetical square of wood measuring 12″ × 12″ × 1″ [30.5 × 30.5 × 2.5cm]. An actual board thickness of one inch is usually stated as 4/4 (four quarters). Other standard wood thicknesses are 5/4, 6/4, 8/4, 10/4, 12/4, 14/4, 16/4.

Hardwood is usually sold K.D.—that is, kiln dried. Under these circumstances the moisture content of the wood will be in the area of 9 percent. Nevertheless, the wood will be sold to you according to a "green measure"; if you order 100 board feet [30.5m] of, say, hard maple, 7 percent will usually be deducted automatically, and you will end with 93 board feet [28.3m], even if you are charged for the full 100.

From private dealers, small sawmills, and the like, you may be able to purchase air-dried lumber that has been stickered outside for a few years. An old rule of thumb to keep in mind when buying such wood stipulates that wood stacked outside dries at the rate of one inch [2.5cm] per year. Air-dried lumber rarely falls below a moisture reading of 10–12 percent, which is not quite good enough for lamination. This means that the woodworker who strikes a bargain buying lumber from a local farmer will have to cart it off to the kiln for drying. Whether or not money is saved this way depends on the original price plus the value the woodworker attaches to his own labors. Green lumber can also be purchased widely, and requires even more processing. It would never be used in its raw state unless for steam-bending.

When buying wood from a dealer, remember that the price break comes at 500 board feet [152.5m]. Ordinarily you will not be allowed to select your wood. If you are, avoid that dealer in the future, for someone else may have selected his wood before you, cleaning out the firsts and leaving you with the seconds. Deal with a lumber company that selects wood for all its customers, and be content to take the seconds with the firsts as they are delivered. Remember, you are always allowed a few rejections.

For lamination purposes I recommend board thicknesses of 5/4 or 6/4. This represents a compromise. Lumber of 8/4 (2"/5cm) thickness allows a quicker lamination procedure. Nevertheless, cross sections may differ so drastically that the section may not reflect the form. Also, 8/4 is not so dimensionally stable as thinner woods. Further, it costs more and is subject to greater wastage. On the other hand, 4/4 lumber may be better so far as stability and price are concerned, but lamination progress with one-inch [2.5 cm] laminae goes very slowly because of the many layers required. A happy medium seems to be one and one quarter or one and one half inches [3.2, 3.8 cm] (5/4 and 6/4).

The best woods for lamination are walnut, cherry, hard maple, and Honduras mahogany. Oak does fairly well. Elm can be used for smaller laminations. Among foreign woods that can be laminated are the aforementioned mahogany as well as teak, rosewood, and zebrawood.

Adhesives

These pages could turn into an exercise in tedium if I were to list and describe all glues available on the market. To attempt such a list would also be an exercise in futility, because some glues are available in one part of the country and not in another and others may have been removed from the market, then upgraded and renamed by the time this book is published.

Suffice it to say that adhesives come in nearly every conceivable form and application. There are glues with high tack and others with low tack. There are glues that serve as fillers. There are waterproof glues, water-resistant glues. There are slow-drying glues, fast-drying glues. There are hot glues and cold glues, plastic glues, hide glues, polyvinyl glues. Despite this rich array, let me confess that in our shop we use ordinary Elmer's carpenter glue for most laminating purposes.

When purchasing glue, be sure to read enough of the label to learn about such crucial factors as shelf life and whether or not freezing can alter the glue's characteristics.

Finishing Materials

Many oil finishes come as patented products, packaged in fancy cans and given important-sounding names. Yet over the years I have become convinced that the best basic oil finish for laminated pieces consists of a simple, three-step process using generic products.

Step 1. Saturate the piece with boiled linseed oil diluted with turpentine. Once this mixture is applied, hand rub the piece to drive the oil deep into the wood pores.

Step 2. The second, third, and fourth coats consist of plain boiled linseed oil. Spread it on, allow to set briefly, then wipe dry completely. A day intervenes between each coat.

Step 3. Mix linseed oil with varnish in a 7:3 or 8:2 ratio. Wipe it on, allow to set briefly, then wipe off.

Other finishes may be used for lamination procedures. In the stack table described in Chapter 7, I employ an ebonized finish, a staining process that turns the wood black. Occasionally pieces are sprayed with lacquer or urethane.

SAFETY

However artistic a woodworker may regard himself, however otherworldly his thoughts and creative his mood, he had better nevertheless develop an utterly bourgeois mentality toward safety if he wishes to continue long in the craft. For woodworkers must deal all day long with machines that have the potential to maim or even kill.

A list of safety rules covering all eventualities could, once more, take up page upon page. But the important ones can be reduced to a handful of easily remembered precepts.

1. A dull machine is a dangerous machine.
2. Safety glasses go on when the power goes on.
3. Secure loose clothing and hair.
4. Never wear gloves when working with power tools.
5. Ears need protection too! Watch those decibels!
6. No alcohol or other consciousness-altering substances before or during work hours.

3.
Design and the Lamination Technique

The design process, when applied to laminated forms, moves in a fairly predictable manner from rough preliminary, or "idea," sketches, to finished sketches, then to scale drawings and even a rendering, which in turn is enlarged to the full-size working drawings used in the actual construction procedures. A three-dimensional scale model may also be a desirable, or even necessary, aspect of the design phase.

A more detailed explanation of these procedures will follow in due course, but it will be useful first to recall the nature of the woodworking made possible by the lamination technique, to wit: work in which the volume of unbroken wood surface is unlimited and the utilization of the curved line is unrestricted.

These factors affect not only the *object* of design, but the *process* itself. In developing ideas that will eventually become pieces of furniture, the wood-worker who avails himself of lamination and carving techniques will not be bound by the geometric demands associated with traditional furniture design. Thus the free sketch tends to replace the more technical strictures of draftsmanship. The designer here approaches his task more like the painter, who begins with charcoal sketches, than like the architect, whose initial considerations are the various engineering factors involved in his overall construction.

The practical consequence for the woodworker is that he will look almost everywhere and anywhere for his basic ideas except in the field of existing furniture. It is likely that he will be aware already that new approaches to furniture forms dependent upon the techniques of contemporary or period furniture are doomed to failure, that almost all possible design ideas have long since been exhausted, that any further exploitation of extant furniture forms is bound to be a case of witting or unwitting plagiarism—for somewhere, sometime, a similar piece has been created.

Nowhere is the limitation of traditional furnituremaking more poignant than that style popularly called "Danish modern." Hardly had the craze for this type of furniture peaked in the late fifties than it showed signs of exhaustion. Why? Mainly because Danish modern was conceived of in terms of a plan and elevation—it was given a front view, a side view, and a back view. In contrast to the almost unlimited possibilities open to those who work in laminated forms, there remained for the Scandinavian designers no real opportunity to explore such promising areas in design as continuity of surface and sculptured form. Because of these limitations, the difference between Danish modern and period furniture turned out to be superficial. One style might end in a claw foot while the other depended on a slick brass ferrule; one might have a simple apron around a table top while the other made use of a carved relief, but in its essentials, Danish modern broke little new ground.

Fig. 3-1. Typical Scandinavian modern design. The lines are clean, symmetrical. Traditional mortise-and-tenon joinery bonds the various components. (Photo: Courtesy of Mobilia Press, Snekkersten, Denmark)

In contrast, the lamination technique opens doors for the furniture designer, allowing his imagination to explore entirely new areas, the only limit being the horizons of his artistic fancies and ingenuity. He can choose from a wide variety of sources for his form ideas. I have already indicated my personal preference for organic forms—these offer an enormous range of design possibilities—but there are innumerable other sources for form studies. For example, the wide world of inorganic forms—rocks, crystals, mechanical objects such as gears, hardware, machinery, not to mention architectural styles—can be transformed by a fertile artistic imagination into exquisite furniture forms.

The choice of area to be explored by the designer ultimately is a highly personal one. Here the artist-craftsman can—and, indeed, must—be as arbitrary as his ego dictates. He need insure only that the object of his muse is sufficiently powerful to sustain the considerable concentration required as he begins to subject his chosen form to his creative powers.

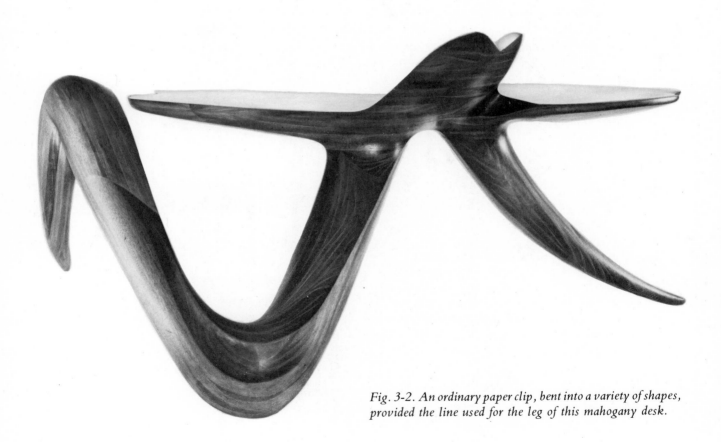

Fig. 3-2. An ordinary paper clip, bent into a variety of shapes, provided the line used for the leg of this mahogany desk.

THE IDEA SKETCH

Once a suitable form has been chosen, the designer must call upon his skill and imagination as he begins, with pencil and paper, the task of metamorphosing form into a functional piece of furniture. The first task is to see the object properly, to explore it with the eye to fully comprehend its uniqueness and beauty. He will study the form from this perspective until he knows it as thoroughly as a painter would. This will entail a suspension of preconceptions, for the designer must be able to see the object in a totally new and fresh manner.

To give a personal example, I have long held a fascination for shells. The primitive, spiraling, emergent lines of, say, a conch shell appear over and over again in my designs. For the past ten years I have had a weathered whelk shell that I take out from time to time for study. And rarely has it failed to suggest a variety of design possibilities for the form problems I am trying to solve.

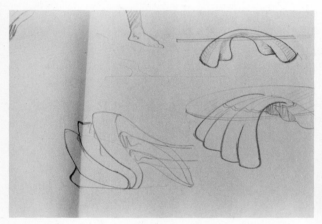 

Fig. 3-3. Sketching involves the exploration of an object with the eye and the imagination. Here shell-like forms are investigated for their potential as table pedestals.

Fig. 3-4. I have used this weathered whelk shell, one of the most ancient organic forms the earth provides, to suggest many of my furniture designs.

Once the designer has studied his chosen form, he will begin those drawing variations from which ideas for a suitable piece of furniture may evolve. At this point the imagination becomes more active; sketches begin to vary widely; ideas are taken up, treated boldly, and quickly set aside. At the idea-sketch phase, the designer must not be afraid of the bad or the grotesque. What is important is that he explore quickly and fearlessly a wide range of possibilities. He should sketch every conceivable variation on the pure form, not contenting himself at this point with two or three solutions. The widest array of possibilities must be investigated in the preliminary phase.

If a particularly good idea occurs to the designer, it is advisable that he resist exploring it until he has exhausted every other preliminary idea that may have occurred to him, even if none seems nearly so promising. A great deal of design time is wasted by woodworkers who settle upon their idea sketch too quickly and do not discover until many frustrating hours later that what seemed like a good idea led nowhere.

Do not be afraid of bad ideas. Sometimes bad ideas have a way of leading to very good ones, which is one reason I always keep my sketches, even those that seemed quite unsatisfactory at the time. The point of the idea sketch is to experiment, to move quickly, even audaciously, through a wide range of design possibilities. As I shall explain farther along, the designer-woodworker has neither the leisure nor the resources to linger for long in the realm of pure design. He must cover a great deal of territory quickly. Soon a few good ideas will begin to emerge. These are then carried forward to the next stage.

Before turning to the subject of perspective drawings, however, let me say that in my discussion of design up to this point, I have assumed that the woodworker has chosen to proceed from pure form toward a functional application. But what about the craftsman who begins his design with a specific result in mind? What if someone brings to the idea sketch phase a determination that he wants from it a table, a liquor cabinet, a chair?

I would offer two observations. First, I recommend to the person just beginning to work in this area to start his studies always by moving from the examination of pure form toward a functional metamorphosis. In this way, he will not only learn how to solve his aesthetic problems, but will also gradually begin to equip his imagination with a variety of forms that will be available later when the design task calls for a more practical approach. Second, the design process that begins from functional considerations will, in any event, not prove too different from that described above. The designer who must conclude his task with a dining table that seats six people will eventually move from the practicalities of his task to imaginative possibilities.

PERSPECTIVE DRAWING

Once the basic idea has been established, the designer begins to refine his drawing in a way that reflects detail and scale. The result of this process will be the perspective drawing, or the final set of sketches prior to the full-scale working drawings.

During this phase the designer will have to fall back upon his knowledge of standard design technique, an area this book will not attempt to treat in a comprehensive manner. Suffice it to say that a thorough grounding in the theory and practice of design is a matter of priority at this point. I can only hope that the advanced woodworker who reads these pages will have some acquaintance with such competent texts in the field as *The Nature and Art of Workmanship,* by David Pye (Van Nostrand Reinhold, 1971). Moreover, he should possess the necessary skills in the areas of workshop geometry and draftsmanship that will enable him to carry his ideas from the realm of pure form into the world of functional construction.

In the perspective-drawing stage of the design process, another concern joins that of the aesthetic. For now the designer must begin to take into account the more mundane demands of actual construction. He will have to be especially careful when sketching a flowing form that he does not gloss over construction techniques, leaving him with an unsolvable technical snafu in the construction phase.

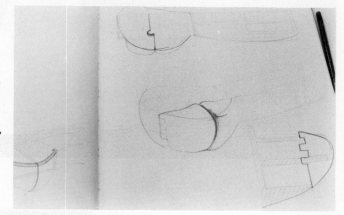

Fig. 3-5. A "flowing" design requires, if anything, a greater attention to mechanical details than does a rectilinear one. This drawing was one of a series of preparatory sketches for a hinge area in a buffet.

There are numerous other considerations to be dealt with at this phase: problems relative to balance, weight, and the like. Among other things, the woodworker must ask himself if his piece might require dismantling.

If moving parts are involved in the item of furniture about to be built, various technical matters must be worked through at this point. As examples, the placement of drawers for a bureau, the correct hinging of doors in a cabinet, the positioning and operation of leaves for an expanding table are considerations that must occupy the designer's attention. The upholstering of furniture carries its own peculiar set of demands, and these too must be worked through at this stage of the design. In all of these matters the designer will fall back on drafting skills and shop experience.

One matter of peculiar importance in the lamination procedure is the necessity for the designer to think in terms of cross sections. This is of such crucial importance that I shall devote to it a more detailed explanation in a separate section. Suffice it to say here that the finished drawing must not be so absorbed with aesthetic strivings that it fails to deal with such humble yet critical matters as where clamps can be positioned.

Fig. 3-6a, b, and c. The problem of providing table leaves for this piece was one that had to be worked out early in the design phase. Maple Dining Table with Leaves (1975): closed, 29 x 56 x 56 in. [73.7 x 142.2 x 142.2cm]; with one leaf, 29 x 56 x 76 in. [193cm]; with two leaves, 29 x 56 x 96 in. [243.8cm]; stack lamination. Private collection.

Once more, the designer should bear in mind the possibility that even at the perspective-drawing stage of the design task, he might best, for one reason or another, abandon the work. He may have reached a dead end for any number of reasons. The item may simply not look right when given perspective. Construction procedures may prove impractical for reasons that develop only when a wider array of considerations has been brought to bear upon the project. It is not inconceivable that a designer might have all but completed his design work, only to be forced to the realization that all his efforts have been for naught.

Even here, though, one must resist the temptation to "fix" the drawing. Whereas this dodge may be effective on a two-dimensional plane, what the novice fails to realize until it is too late is that it has served only to transfer his difficulties into the more exacting area of three-dimensional construction.

No amount of warning here is apt to dissuade the apprentice. He will learn the lesson primarily at the painful level of trial and error. Only after considerable vexation does the woodworker-designer begin to realize that the point of design is not the creation of good drawings, but the resolution of problems—practical as well as aesthetic ones.

Not only are construction and mechanical problems worked out in the perspective-drawing stage, but the final design subtleties are taken care of then as well. The arm of a chair might not look exactly right; the relation of a tabletop to its base may seem slightly disproportionate. The problems are minor and can be worked through without much difficulty.

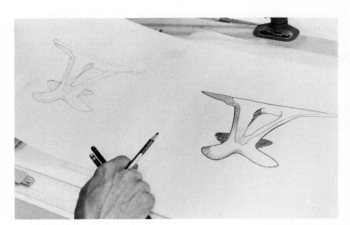

Fig. 3-7. The overlay method enables the designer to separate quickly the desirable elements from the undesirable, and to improve on the latter.

At this point, the designer can save a great deal of time by tracing out that part of the design already acceptable and then, for the rest, making such variations as seem desirable. Various modifications can be tried on until a measure of artistic satisfaction is achieved.

The result of the perspective drawings will be a set of scale drawings presenting the object from its front or most characteristic orientation. These will likely be accompanied by additional drawings offering a variety of perspectives. These latter are of particular importance for woodworkers who have difficulty "reading" drawings, which is to say they find it hard to imagine that aspect of the piece that does not present itself in the front rendering.

Details are worked along the margins, or on a separate piece of paper.

MODELS

Sketching tends to be a test of drawing skills. At issue for the designer is whether or not he can commit to paper what his mind has visualized. Some designers have more aptitude at this sort of thing than do others. Those less capable with a pencil may find it helpful to work through design problems with a scale model.

Lest anyone detect a note of condescension here, let me quickly confess that I make considerable use of models myself. I do so especially when complicated forms have evolved or when the three-dimensional aspect is particularly difficult to conceptualize. If constructed absolutely to scale— ordinarily I use a one inch to one foot [2.5cm:30.5cm] ratio—the model itself can be used as an adjunct to, or a substitute for, a working drawing.

Fig. 3-8. I started the design of a grandfather's clock in a contemporary mode with a clay model at a scale of one inch to one foot [2.5cm:30.5cm].

A model provides a particular advantage in the lamination procedure, especially when stacking begins at the bottom of the piece. In such a case, the model can be turned upside down, so that the bottom—the first layer of lamination—can be accurately visualized. Also, for cross-sectional considerations, a model can be cut in half to allow it to be viewed from that perspective.

There are numerous other advantages to working with models. Mechanical problems are particularly amenable to solution through the use of models; if a malleable substance like clay is used, the designer can work through questions about form that seem especially difficult through the very process of modeling the clay. It should be mentioned in passing that models are of enormous help in presenting a proposal to prospective clients.

Clay, incidentally, is a particularly appropriate medium for the development of plastic forms. Various other materials can also be used for models, among them styrofoam, papier-mâché, plaster of paris, balsa wood, and wax.

CROSS-SECTIONAL CONSIDERATIONS

I single out for extended discussion the necessity of thinking in terms of cross sections when dealing with laminated forms so that its importance will not be overlooked. The primary reason to consider the work in cross section is that the walls of a project must be built as thinly as possible without compromising either design or the inherent strength of the piece.

Many people are under the impression that a form carved from wood laminations begins as one huge chunk of wood from which are removed only those parts necessary to permit the design form to emerge—a process rather like a sculptor chipping away fragments of marble. This is not at all the case. Although laminated forms often give the appearance of massiveness and although many of them are indeed of considerable weight, the fact is that most are hollow, and this for reasons of no little consequence.

Again, what is the critical factor here? Does the woodworker strive for the thinnest possible walls primarily in the interests of wood economy? Not entirely, although this factor does enter in. The cost of select hardwoods is high, and going higher. There seems little reason to use massive quantities of wood that serve no useful purpose, save only to invest the illusion of mass with the fact.

Weight considerations also enter the picture. Hollow forms permit a reasonable weight for pieces of greater than average size and surface area. Surely nothing is to be gained by creating a piece of furniture that cannot be supported by an ordinary floor joist or that poses a test of endurance for the furniture mover.

The most critical factor, however, has to do with dimensional stability. As was noted earlier, wood takes on and releases moisture from its outer surface. As wood thickness increases, the tensions created by expansion and contraction because of humidity develop accordingly. Given sufficient bulk, even the most expertly laminated wood can crack simply because of internal stress brought about by ordinary changes in humidity.

The use of hollow forms tends to defeat this in two ways. First, it reduces the stress area, and second, it nearly doubles the wood surface, exposing a much larger area of the form to the outer air, which leads to a more even rate of expansion and contraction throughout the piece.

From the point of view of construction, the cross-sectional sketch enables the woodworker to begin his project correctly and to end it correctly. Without a top, or "plan," view, a flowing design can quickly move out of control. The answer here is carefully worked out cross-section drawings.

Fig. 3-9. Moisture considerations aside, the weight of a piece often dictates a hollow construction. Had this 175-pound [79kg] piece been of solid construction throughout, it would have weighed in the neighborhood of 300 pounds [136kg]. Walnut Desk (1976): 30 x 40 x 75 in. [76.2 x 101.6 x 190.5cm]; stack lamination. Private collection.

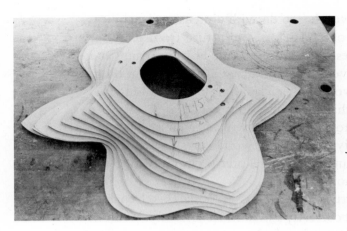

Fig. 3-10. Templates for the pedestal of a table indicate the extent to which laminated forms require cross-sectional planning.

WORKING DRAWINGS

Inasmuch as laminated forms do not rely so heavily on the kind of geometric designs associated with shop draftsmanship, it is necessary to complete the design process by enlarging the perspective drawings to full scale. These, then, become the working drawings and, in certain instances, actually act as patterns.

For this purpose I use a thirty-six-inch [91cm] width of butcher's white kraft paper tacked to an oversize plywood easel. If necessary, the paper can be overlapped. A grid system can be used for purposes of enlargement; it provides far greater accuracy than does a free-hand effort.

TWO RESERVATIONS

Having described the typical design process I employ, I feel obliged to conclude with some precautionary reflections. The first has to do with lack of design time, the second with lack of design talent.

To begin with, it should be evident that the woodworker has neither the time nor the resources to investigate the design aspects of his work to the same degree as does a professional designer. The design phase for the woodworker, in other words, has built-in limitations, and not only as regards time. He does not, in addition, have the opportunity to engage in the kind of testing and marketing investigation associated with high-volume manufacture. The woodworker has no time for prototypes, for lengthy consultations, for inter-disciplinary evaluation or wide-ranging programs of research.

I would question, in any event, that the practicing craftsman with such skills at his disposal could turn out a better design than, say, Joe Colombo, Charles Eames, or Ettore Sottsass. This may not be due to aesthetic inferiority, but to the different demands that pertain to two quite different disciplines.

For example, the woodworker remains bound to a craft tradition extending back over many centuries; however avant-garde his work may appear, the underlying techniques tend to conserve a tradition of great antiquity. No wood craftsman can fail to appreciate the skills that have developed over the centuries, nor be unaware of his responsibility to preserve them and teach them to apprentices. The designer, by contrast, is interested not only in new forms, but in new materials and new techniques of construction as well. His is an effort at change at all levels, whereas the woodworker tends to be limited by the venerable nature of his craft.

A second warning regards the undeniable fact that not all woodworkers possess design talents. Design capabilities are, after all, just that—talent. It is a gift, one that has nothing to do with industriousness or virtue. The simple truth is that there are many superb woodworkers who have very little talent for design as such. Whereas they possess enormous gifts in the area of woodworking itself, theirs is not a visualizing or creative capacity.

What gives this situation poignancy is the fact that although it is certainly possible to improve by instruction and practice whatever design capacities one has been given, the basic knack of design simply cannot be imparted at a teaching level.

For many years, while a professor at the Rochester Institute of Technology's School for American Craftsmen, I worked under the delusion that design capabilities could be taught. The result was a number of extremely frustrated students, who otherwise were exceptionally skilled in their field.

Unfortunately, most woodworking students feel that the design aspect of the woodworking task is an integral part of the process, that if a craftsman fails here he fails in all aspects of his work. This judgment is, in my opinion, open to question. Certainly in the field of music the performer is not expected to be proficient in all areas of the musical arts, nor is a composer expected necessarily to be a gifted instrumentalist. An attitude comparable to what prevails in the woodworking field would demand that a performer not only play music, but compose it too, and perhaps build his instrument besides.

I do not suggest that the craftsman who excels in woodworking technique should necessarily forego the study of design, but there is no reason why the sources of his design should not come either through collaborative efforts or through the application of extant designs.

Each woodworker must decide for him or herself the extent of this talent. Such evaluation may have its painful moments, but the overall results will more than offset the anguish that comes of self-delusion. The ancient dictum "Know thyself" applies to woodworkers as well as to anyone else.

4.

Bentwood Lamination

In the chapters to follow we will take up the four basic lamination procedures one by one, giving each technique a chapter of generalized description followed by a chapter in which that technique is illustrated by a particular construction. Let us begin with the technique known as *bentwood lamination*.

BACKGROUND AND DESCRIPTION

The molecular structure of wood is such that when it is bent two predictable results will follow. First, wood will tolerate a limited amount of curvature. Second, bent beyond that limit the wood will crack. A third predictable in dealing with wood is that when the bending pressure is eased, the wood will tend to return to its original shape. This result may be immediate, as when wood virtually snaps back into place, or it may be a drawn-out process, lasting over a period of months or even years. In either case, wood retains a memory of its original shape so powerful and so persistent that it must be reckoned with.

Thus, before a woodworker bends wood for a particular purpose, he must not only take into account stress factors that may lead to cracking, but he must also devise ways of defeating wood's inherent tendency to resume its original configuration. Of the various options, the bentwood lamination technique provides a particularly effective solution.

In simplest terms, the bentwood procedure involves the sawing of a single board into strips flexible enough to assume a desired curve without fracturing, then reassembling, gluing, bending, and clamping these strips to a mold. When the glue has set, an adhesive power greater than the elasticity of the wood molecules will have permanently secured the wood to the desired shape. The wood will have lost its memory, as it were, and assumed a stable curve that accords with the woodworker's specifications.

This lamination technique has any number of applications, both aesthetic and practical. It is particularly useful in making wooden forms that require a thin, graceful line and, therefore, demand a maximum of strength with a minimum of wood. Because laminated bentwood can be incredibly strong—far stronger than the inherent strength of the board from which the laminae were sawn—the woodworker is free to design slender and elaborate elements that are nevertheless capable of bearing weight. The legs or pedestals of chairs, tables, cabinets, and so forth, can give an appearance of great delicacy, all the while possessing very nearly the strength of steel.

There is nothing new to the bentwood lamination technique. For centuries furnituremakers achieved curved effects in cabinetry by this procedure. Ordinarily, the inner laminae were taken from common wood stock, while the outer layer was composed of a fine veneer.

It was not until the mid-nineteenth century, however, that Michael Thonet adapted the technique to a style that was simultaneously functional and decorative. The famous Thonet chair (1876) was perhaps the first example of laminated bentwood used in a total design concept. Later, when Thonet's chair had gained immense popularity, the lamination technique was abandoned in favor of bending with steam for reasons of production efficiency.

Fig. 4-1. The Thonet design was one of the first to use a bentwood technique for a combined structural and decorative purpose. A steam process came to be used for bending the wood in lieu of the earlier lamination technique. (Chair and photo: Thonet Industries Inc., York, PA)

Many other designers and craftsmen have employed the lamination technique to great advantage. Alvar Aalto, the Finnish architect, designed a number of pieces that depend upon this process, and his work, carried out mainly during the 1930s, proved ingenious in exploiting the technique.

Fig. 4-2. Alvar Aalto utilized the bentwood process to provide his furniture with this clean, graceful line. Shown here, the Scroll Chair. (Photo: Courtesy of ICF, New York)

The bentwood lamination process has come back into favor with woodworkers in recent years. This is due in part to significant advances in the technology of adhesives. The contemporary woodworker has at his disposal a wide variety of glues that provide considerable versatility in both application and function.

Another reason for the advancing popularity of laminated bentwood is the current interest in flowing lines in the form of furniture. Many factors, among them the influence of art nouveau, have tended to free furniture design from static forms.

STEAMED BENTWOOD

Let us at the outset distinguish between the process of bending wood through sawing and regluing and the more common method of curving wood known as *steam bending*. The latter procedure depends upon steaming, soaking, or heating—or any combination of the three—to sufficiently disturb the molecular structure of the wood that it can be curved into a reasonably permanent form.

For most woodworkers, steam bending is an inferior process to that of lamination. To begin with, steaming weakens wood whereas lamination strengthens it. Steaming tends also to destroy the natural beauty of wood, which is why steam-bent pieces are usually heavily stained. Lamination, on the other hand, often enhances the flow and color of wood in its natural state.

Finally, laminated bentwood is far more stable than its steamed counterpart. Unless formed with highly exacting machinery, steam-bent pieces can behave with notorious unpredictability.

In short, for many craftsmen, the lamination method of bending wood is far and away the better of the two. It requires but a modest outlay of funds for necessary equipment. It allows a degree of predictability that simply cannot be expected of steamed bentwood. And it assures a far higher degree of component strength.

The bentwood procedure can be adapted to a variety of woodworking needs. For example, chair shells can be made using a plywood method of bending wood—the same process, incidentally, used to give a grand piano its characteristic curve. Thin layers of wood are glued together in a cross-grained fashion. An odd number of plys (3, 5, 7, and so forth) is used so that the grain of both outer surfaces will run in the same direction. The glued laminae are clamped to a curved mold, and thereby adopt a permanent bend.

Fig. 4-3. Plys of Italian poplar being glued and formed over a mold. These will become the backs of chairs.

GENERAL PROCEDURES

In Chapter 5 I will show how the laminated bentwood process is applied to the construction of my music rack. I would like to begin, however, with some words of a more general nature to make the reader aware of the basic principles of the technique.

Mold

The first step in the bentwood technique is the construction of a mold. A mold ordinarily consists of several thicknesses of scrap plywood or chipboard sandwiched together to a thickness capable of accommodating the wood laminae and of providing sufficient lateral strength to withstand the various stresses involved.

Once the boards have been sandwiched, the next step is to mark on the mold surface a line to match the curve it is to take. This may be done in a variety of ways, perhaps the easiest being simply to cut out the line and trace its edge directly upon the face of the mold. Should you wish, however, to insure that the wooden strips you will be using are able to take the intended curve, you can bend a sample strip along the line, securing it with finishing nails driven through the working drawing. Then remove the drawing, reinsert the strip, and trace a pencil line along its curve.

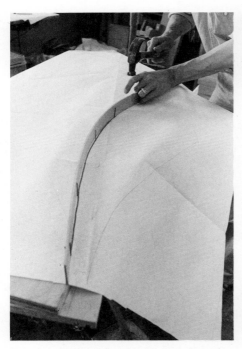

Fig. 4-4. Nailing flexible lamina along the intended curve. Nails are driven through the scale drawing to the plywood mold beneath.

Fig. 4-5. The drawing having been lifted free of the nails, the strip is then reinserted along the nailed track and a line traced across the mold.

Although there are occasions when a woodworker has the choice between a male (convex) mold and a female (concave) mold, in this case a male mold is preferable, mainly because it is easier to wrap wooden strips over an exterior surface than it is to push them into an interior space.

Once you have transferred the line to the plywood, saw the mold to shape on the band saw. Ordinarily, I cut out the rough, or backing, side first. This reduces bulk and permits me to saw more accurately along the mold line. After band-sawing, remove imperfections with a spokeshave, then sand the mold surface smooth and wax it to prevent glue seizing.

Fig. 4-6. Layers of scrap plywood face-glued together become the raw material of bentwood molds. Here I band-saw the basic shape of the mold, beginning with the underside of the curve.

Fig. 4-7. Smoothing the surface of the mold with a spokeshave.

When the mold is finished, it is time to determine the proper thickness for the laminae with which you will work. (If you have used the nailing method for tracing the line, this determination has already been made.) Needless to say, the more exaggerated the curve, the thinner the strips must be. A very gentle bend will accommodate laminations in the vicinity of one-quarter inch [6.4mm], whereas a tight curve may require strips as thin as one-sixteenth inch [1.6mm] or even less.

In passing, we should note that extremely tight curves present a number of difficulties, not least of which is clamp interference. If extreme curvature is required, you may have to make a double mold, or you may have to fall back on another form of lamination, such as stack or scarf lamination.

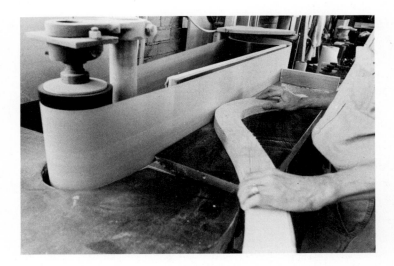

Fig. 4-8. Giving the mold a final sanding.

Wood Selection

Some woods are bent more easily than others. Straight-grained woods like oak, ash, cherry, and walnut adapt more readily to the process than, say, tropical woods like berbinga, African mahogany, or zebrawood. Still, I know of no woods that cannot be made to bend to some degree. Oak is a particularly desirable wood for the bentwood method. Its grain tends to be so regular and coarse that lamination lines are virtually indetectable. Regardless of the wood used, examine your stock carefully to make sure that you select boards that are straight-grained and free from imperfections. Plane rough boards if the grain does not manifest itself.

Moisture content should be tested as a matter of course. Although levels are not so critical in bentwood lamination as, for example, in stack lamination, the wood should not contain more than 10 percent moisture.

Ordinarily, the board thickness will not exceed two inches [5cm]. If for some reason you require a broader curved surface, make identical multiples of the bentwood form and assemble them by jointing and gluing.

This bentwood technique imposes limitations of length as well. Five- or even six-foot [1.5,1.8m] pieces of laminated bentwood can be fabricated with some degree of ease, but beyond that length difficulties begin to manifest themselves: Sawing becomes exceedingly exacting, requiring the presence of a competent assistant; glues may start to set before clamping is completed. The best idea, if longer bentwood pieces are desired, is again to use multiples; in this case, they will have to be spliced, not jointed.

It hardly needs to be stated that construction problems of this nature should be worked through at the design phase.

Sawing

Having selected a straight-grained piece of stock, begin the sawing procedure by setting the table saw to the predetermined thickness. For this purpose I use a 45-tooth carbide-tipped combination blade; if properly operated, it can cut strips sufficiently smoothly to require no further jointing.

If you wish to omit the jointing stage, you must take extra time at this point to insure that the saw is set up correctly. The blade must be set at an exact right angle to the table. Insert a "splitter" beyond the blade to prevent the wood from pinching on the saw and to keep the strip from falling into the blade. Finally, set the fence precisely so that there will be no taper, no tendency for the blade to bind or burn. A plastic shield may be attached, to prevent sawdust from flying around excessively.

Fig. 4-9. No taper is allowable in the resawing of laminae strips. Use a square to check that the blade is at a perfect right angle to the table.

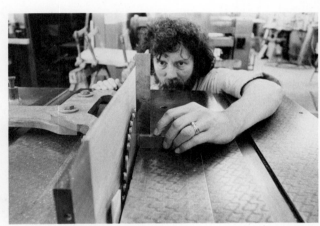

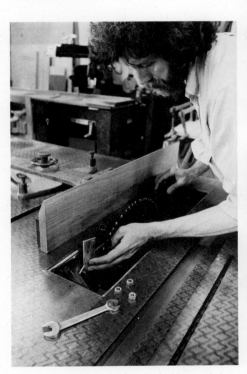

Fig. 4-10. A "splitter" inserted beyond the blade insures a clean separation in the sawing process.

Fig. 4-11. The primary purpose of a plastic shield is to protect the woodworker's face and guarantee clear visibility throughout sawing procedures. This device, used in conjunction with a vacuum system, will remove all but a negligible amount of sawdust.

If sawing is to be followed immediately by gluing, without the intervening steps of planing and jointing, you must feed the wood through the saw in one continuous flow. If the blade rotates more in one spot than at other points along the cut, an imperfect gluing surface will result. This, by the way, is one of the reasons why working with long pieces is problematical.

Whatever the size of the wood, the woodworker unacquainted with this procedure should work with an assistant when ripping the wood. The more experienced woodworker can do this procedure alone—up to a point. It may be reassuring to know that a cut spoiled in sawing can be corrected on the planer.

Before cutting the laminae, pencil two diagonal marks along the top of the board to insure that the strips will be reassembled in precisely the order and orientation in which they were cut.

Fig. 4-12. Cutting longer laminae requires the services of a skilled assistant. Note the word skilled. Amateurs are of no help here, given the requirements of positioning and even feed of the wood.

Fig. 4-13. A moment taken to draw a pair of pencil lines diagonally across the board about to be resawn will insure positive reassembly should the strips fall out of sequence.

Jointing and Planing—An Alternative Method

An alternative method of preparing the wood strips for bentwood lamination involves an intermediate step using a jointer and planer. This procedure permits less precision at the sawing stage.

Begin by running the edge of the board to be resawn through the jointer. Saw this side of the board to the desired thickness and set aside the resulting strip. Again pass the sawn surface on the larger stock through the jointer. Another cut, and the second strip is set aside. Proceed in this manner, jointing, sawing, jointing, sawing, and so forth.

When done, you are left with a series of strips jointed on one side. Next pass the sawn sides through the power planer. For this operation, place the strips on a waxed board, which can move through the planer and support the flexible strips so they will not be deformed by the feeding mechanism.

Fig. 4-14. Jointing the remaining stock after every sawing will insure one perfectly flat side for bentwood laminae.

Fig. 4-15. The planer provides an opposing flat edge. Feed strips through the planer on a waxed board.

What is gained by this intermediate step is a slightly higher degree of precision along the gluing surfaces. There are, however, disadvantages to the procedure. For example, a grain imperfection may cause a strip of wood to be pulverized by the planer. In this event, you may find yourself with a grain mismatch or perhaps a shortage of strips, and you may be obliged to begin the process all over again. The wise woodworker will allow for a few extra laminae.

Gluing

In Chapter 2 I made some general comments on the various commercial glues available to the woodworker; this discussion is available for review. Before engaging in laminated bentwood procedures, you should have a thorough understanding of the properties and applications of the many wood adhesives available. This will prevent you from, say, utilizing a quick-setting glue that will begin to harden before you can complete a complex clamping operation. You should also be aware that certain glues tend to raise the glue line when exposed to moisture or air, and that certain oily woods—teak and rosewood, for example—do better with a catalyst-type glue like resorcinol or epoxy than with one of the polyvinyl glues.

The gluing process itself must move along quickly and efficiently. All necessary materials, including a sufficient number of clamps, should be close by. The mold should be ready, clamped to a convenient worktable. Backup strips to accept the mark of the clamp and distribute pressure should be on hand and the lamination strips prepared and in sequence.

Apply the glue rapidly in an even and generous coat to only one of the surfaces to be glued (there is no need to glue two facing surfaces, no matter what the label instructs). A small paint roller or brush may be used, though a wooden shim—or squeegee—will serve just as well.

Fig. 4-16. Glue is applied quickly to the bentwood laminae with a piece of scrapwood or a squeegee.

Quickly assemble the glued pieces and press them onto the backing strip along the mold. Position the outside backing strip and apply the first clamp. The placement of the initial clamp will differ according to the situation. Sometimes it is placed in the center of the laminations, especially if a female mold is being used. At other times it may be fixed to one end or the other.

Before adding a second clamp, carefully examine the position of the wood strips relative to one another. This can be critical since the pieces have the tendency to splay out like an elongated deck of cards. Take a little extra time here—but not too much! Hand-screw clamps at either end may help control the tendency of the laminae to splay.

Finally, add the rest of the clamps—as many as the backing strips and mold will accommodate.

When all clamps are in place, tighten them one last time and then leave the laminations to set overnight.

Having described the basic technique of bentwood lamination, we can now turn to its practical application in the construction of a music rack.

Fig. 4-18. Finally, tighten all clamps. A back strip takes the indentation of the clamps.

Fig. 4-17. If the stack of bentwood laminae shows a tendency to splay, use wooden hand-screw clamps to secure the ends.

5.

A Bentwood Music Rack

The idea for my music rack evolved in the year 1963. It began with a few prototypes, but quickly developed into the form that I have here once more undertaken. This same piece was the subject of the 1964 sound film, "The Music Rack,"* which received a number of awards and is still today widely shown, as much a tribute to its maker, Tom Muir Wilson, as to anything else.

As I originally conceived the idea, the music rack would be an artistic investigation of a treelike form. The legs would be rootlike, embracing the ground in a gentle but regular, organic curve. From them the trunk would ascend like a supple, bent sapling. A twiglike appendage would descend to hold the easel.

The components of the music rack consist entirely of bentwood laminations. The easel contains four nearly identical laminations, one of which is extended into a small shelf to hold the music. The remainder of the music rack is but four pieces: two supporting legs, the main trunk, and the descending stem that supports the rosewood slats.

For this particular version of the music rack, I chose a piece of 8/4 white oak. Any one of various other hardwoods could have been used, but oak seemed particularly apposite; not only does it contain a coarse and exceedingly regular grain, but it is among the more flexible of the hardwoods.

*The film may be rented from Your Portable Museum, American Crafts Council, 22 W. 55 St., New York, NY 10019.

Fig. 5-1. *One of my earliest sketches for the music rack, this one dating from the early 1960s.*

I cut two lengths of rough-sawn timber with the radial-arm saw. From the shorter of the two would come the laminae for the legs and stem; the longer stock would provide the lamination strips for the main trunk.

Wood preparation began with jointing one face and one edge of each board. There was no need to prepare the wood further since all I required were one flat face for the table of the variety saw and one flat edge for the fence.

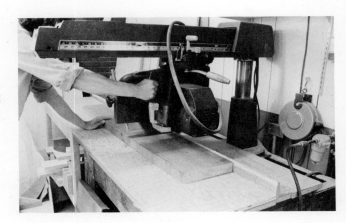

Fig. 5-2. *An eight-foot [2.4m] piece of 8/4 white oak stock is all I needed for the basic structure of the bentwood music rack.*

The procedure I planned to follow did not include the intermediate step of jointing and planing the strips. Accordingly, I carefully prepared the variety saw as outlined in Chapter 4: I set the blade precisely, installed a splitter on the far side of the blade, and placed a plastic shield over the blade. Because the pieces were relatively short, I planned to handle them unassisted.

I had already determined that the strips from the shorter of the two boards could be cut at one-quarter inch [6.4mm] and would take the curves without any difficulty. I needed a total of fifteen strips for the two legs and the stem. For the larger piece, however, a tighter curve was involved; six strips cut to three-sixteenths inch [4.7mm] were required.

I drew a diagonal line across the edge of the boards prior to sawing to insure that the cut strips would be reassembled properly.

Fig. 5-3. Laminae resawn to a thickness of one-quarter inch [6.4mm] will accommodate the curve of the leg without danger of fracturing.

I began my laminating with the trunk. With the mold clamped to a worktable and an adequate supply of clamps standing by, I applied a generous coating of polyvinyl glue to one side of each strip.

As soon as I had coated all six laminae with glue, I laid the stack of strips upon the mold and secured it with a single clamp in the center. Before adding further quick-action clamps, I placed wooden hand-screw clamps vertically along the ends of the strips to prevent the laminae from splaying. I followed with additional quick-action clamps, working from the center toward the ends, placing them at a distance of about three inches [7.6cm] on center.

When the glue had fully set, I removed from the mold the permanently bent trunk member.

I repeated this procedure for the three remaining elements of the music rack before turning my attention to the rosewood slats.

Fig. 5-4. Clamping bentwood laminae to a mold. Hand-screw clamps at either end minimize a tendency for the strips to splay. Note the backup strip.

Fig. 5-5. Completing the clamping process. Quick-action clamps are spaced at about three inches [7.6mm] on centers.

Fig. 5-6. With clamps in place, the form is given a final inspection, then left to set overnight.

Because rosewood acts quite differently from white oak, certain modifications in the lamination process were required. Rosewood does not bend readily, and it fractures easily. Therefore, even though the arc of the slats was very slight, I sawed the laminae to a thickness of one-eighth inch [3.2mm]. Then also, because rosewood tends to be an oily wood, I used a different type of glue—in this case, cascamite.

Fig. 5-7. Rosewood laminae for the slats of the music rack are cut to thickness of one-eighth inch [3.2mm] and, because of the oily consistency of rosewood, secured with a waterproof glue.

Fig. 5-8. The eight basic components of the music rack beside their respective molds.

Laminations removed from any mold require an initial cleaning. Excess glue must first be scraped away. In my shop, we prefer an ordinary paint scraper for this task. Further refinement is done with a hand plane and with the jointer.

One side of the laminated member having been given a finished edge, its parallel surface remained as it came from the mold, covered with dribbles of dried glue. The easiest way of finishing this edge is simply to run its jointed opposite along the fence of the variety saw; the carbide-tipped blade leaves a perfectly parallel mate.

Fig. 5-9. Removing excess glue with a paint scraper.

Fig. 5-10. Using a hand plane to further clean edges.

Fig. 5-11. Next a jointer provides flatness for one edge.

Fig. 5-12. Giving the opposite edge a parallel surface on the variety saw.

Shaping the legs came next. I began by marking the basic taper line and band-sawing. Next, I shaped the contour with a spokeshave, then removed the facets left by the spokeshave with a cabinet rasp.

After this shaping had been completed, I turned my attention to the segment of the leg that would be bonded to the other two members. I smoothed a long surface on the jointer in preparation for creating a scarflike joint.

Fig. 5-13. Band-sawing the taper in the leg.

Fig. 5-14. Initial shaping of the legs is done with an old-fashioned spokeshave.

Fig. 5-15. Using a cabinet rasp to remove facets left behind by the spokeshave.

At this point in the procedure I was able to fall back on earlier experience and save myself considerable time. I knew that once the three legs were assembled, the area near their joining would be exceedingly difficult to sand. Working sandpaper in corners and grooves can be maddening. So I knew that the time for such sanding was now, prior to assembly. I gave the pieces a coarse and a finish sanding on the pneumatic drum sander. The legs and trunk were then ready to be joined together.

Fig. 5-16. Sanding the legs on a pneumatic drum sander. This task is more efficiently accomplished prior to the joining of the legs.

I began by drawing pencil lines to indicate the precise position of these elements relative to one another. I then applied glue to the scarf joints and bonded the three elements, using a half dozen or so quick-action clamps.

While the glue was setting, I turned my attention to the rosewood slats. After a finish sanding, I placed each into position on the stem and pencilled on notch dimensions for each. The depth of the notches was uniformly scribed with the help of a marking gauge. Next, I used a dovetail saw to incise the sides of the notches and, with a flat chisel, removed intervening wood.

Fig. 5-17. A long, scarflike joint bonds the legs of the music rack.

Fig. 5-18. Scribing an accurate line for the notching procedures with a knife.

Fig. 5-19. Notch depths on the trunk are accurately scribed with a marking gauge.

Fig. 5-20. A dovetail saw incises the notches.

Fig. 5-21. *Removing the intervening wood with a flat chisel.*

When I had completed this work, it was time to remove the clamps from the leg joints. I shaped and refined the area around the joints until the joints themselves were all but invisible. Where the legs split apart, I employed a chisel for minor sculpting.

Fig. 5-22. *Sculpting leg jointings with a spokeshave.*

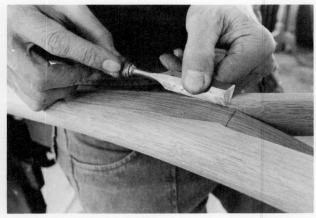

Fig. 5-23. *Refining the junction area of legs and trunk with a chisel.*

At this point the work was beginning to show its final form. The stem was the next item to be fitted to the upright members. Since the jointer could not accommodate the bonding surface, I had to hand-plane it to a perfect flatness.

Fig. 5-24. A hand plane flattens the trunk of the music rack in preparation for the application of the stem.

When finishing by hand, and therefore without the inherent accuracy of power machinery, one must always double-check finished parts to insure a perfect match. Figure 5-25 shows the stem and trunk being viewed against the light to insure that the surfaces to be glued meet exactly all along the line.

Fig. 5-25. A visual inspection of the joint helps insure a perfect mating.

When satisfied that this was the case, I applied glue and clamped the two elements together.

Before bonding the slats to the stem, I inserted them into their respective notches one last time to insure correct tolerances. Then I glued them into place, using small quick-action clamps.

Fig. 5-26. The music rack prior to the installation of rosewood slats. The predominating motif is one of the organic form —root and trunk and stem forming a flowing composite. There remains virtually no evidence of the lamination procedures involved.

Fig. 5-27. Rosewood slats are dry-fitted prior to final gluing into place.

I further anchored the rosewood slats with ebony pins whittled to have a round point and a square shank. The ebony dowels were inserted into drilled holes round end first; when driven home, the square shank forced corners onto the round holes, giving the rather pleasing appearance of a square peg.

The music rack was then given its final hand-sanding and finished with a mixture of boiled linseed oil and turpentine.

Fig. 5-28. *Drilling holes for the ebony pins.*

Fig. 5-29. *The shank of the pin starts round, but ends square.*

Fig. 5-30. *The ebony pins anchor the slats to the stem.*

Fig. 5-31. *Prior to oiling it, I give the music rack a final hand-sanding.*

Fig. 5-32. *The oil solution is applied with a rag and hand-rubbed, which forces the oil deep into the pores of the wood.*

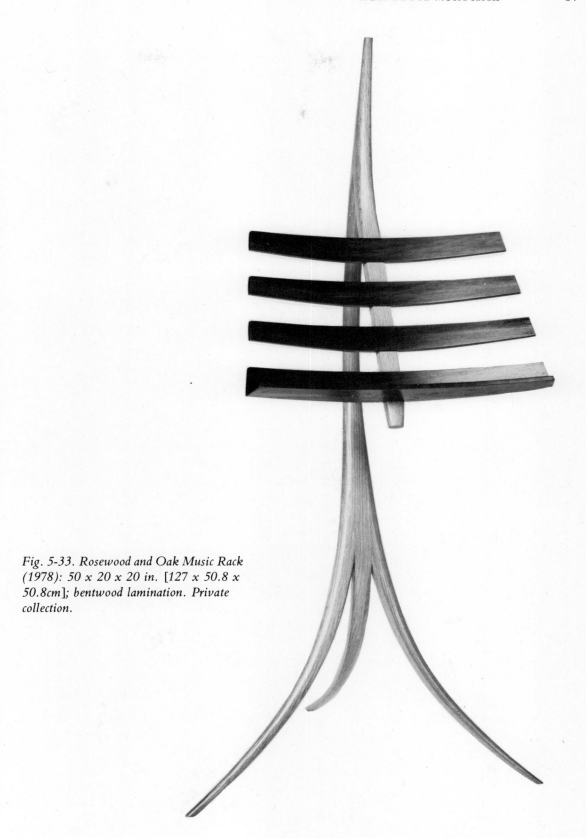

Fig. 5-33. Rosewood and Oak Music Rack (1978): 50 x 20 x 20 in. [127 x 50.8 x 50.8cm]; bentwood lamination. Private collection.

6.

Stack Lamination

Stack lamination is a process in which flat boards are precut to shape, then both face- and edge-glued in such a manner that an overall form, with grain running the same direction, can be built up. The resulting shaped, yet rough-surfaced mass is then further refined by carving and finishing. Stack lamination allows the kind of design continuity and mass that has traditionally been associated with sculpture, but rarely with the fabrication of furniture. By this method the furnituremaker is able to create an integrated sculptural statement.

Although the application of stack lamination procedures to the construction of furniture is a relatively recent development, the principle of layering wood in this manner is quite ancient. In the Middle Ages the carvers of religious statuary would often glue together pieces, or "balks," of wood and then chisel out the form. While with the U.S. Army in postwar Germany, I was able to see many examples of this process. The techniques were crude and the glues inadequate. Several layers of paint were used to conceal technical deficiencies, but the flaking away of the polychrome revealed such features as the pegging of limbs to torsos, presumably because the craftsmen did not know how properly to joint the elements. Nevertheless, the essential technique is a forerunner of modern stack lamination.

Fig. 6-1. Detail of wooden statue of Christ dated 1147, showing dowelled jointure. (Museo de Arte de Cataluna, Barcelona, Spain; photo: Courtesy of Hirmer Fotoarchiv, Munich, Germany)

Other applications of the principle come to mind, some of them quite commonplace. During the Second World War, and for some time thereafter, the construction of solid balsa model airplanes by means of a lamination technique was a popular pastime. Cross sections were shaped and glued together to obtain a rough shape of the fuselage, which was then sanded to its final form. Aside from model planes, other wood objects such as floating decoys lend themselves to this technique. In the nineteenth century laminated wood was used to craft carousel horses and cigar store Indians. And the technique continues to be used today. Sculptors in wood, among them Leonard Baskin, begin their creations with a large, laminated block of wood much as though it were a slab of marble.

What contributions I have made to the technique apply mainly to the creation of furniture with flowing lines. In a more technical sense, however, my major offering derives from a more detailed attention to the advantages of cross-sectioning than has been customary in the lamination procedure. I have developed a method of building up forms with strict adherence to scale renderings and considerations of the cross section, with the result that the original laminations closely approximate—within fractions of an inch—the form of the eventual object. This approach allows the development of hollow forms that give the illusion of mass, yet provides for moisture equalization within the wood fibers and, hence, a lessening of internal stress and the consequent risk of splitting or fracturing.

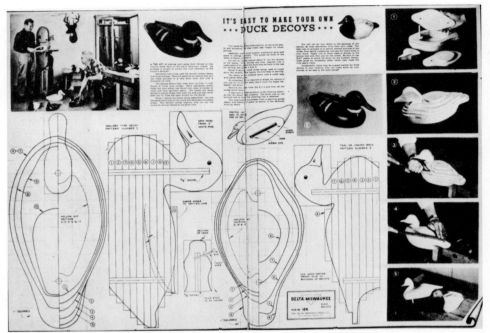

Fig. 6-2. Plans for a laminated duck decoy provide a simple yet comprehensive description of basic stack lamination techniques. (From Deltagram *[September-October 1944], Pittsburgh: Rockwell International)*

On the whole, stack lamination is a far more demanding procedure than bentwood lamination. Because of the greater area of wood surface involved and because the form is frequently more elaborate or complicated, a number of factors become critical. Wood must be selected with great care. Moisture levels must be checked at the outset to assure wood compatability. Jointing and planing must be accurate, with all edges parallel and square.

First-rate equipment is required for stack lamination. It need not be expensive, but must be accurate and well maintained. And by all means, basic cabinet shop techniques will have to have been mastered in advance.

In spite of such precautionary statements, I would not hesitate to encourage skilled amateurs to experiment with the technique. It can be a most fascinating alternative to the more standard woodworking procedures. As for professional woodworkers, an acquaintance with stack lamination techniques is an absolute necessity; for although very few cabinetmakers or woodworkers will rely on the procedure for the greater part of their work, they will occasionally find it a most practical resource in solving quite ordinary woodworking problems.

SELECTING AND PREPARING THE WOOD

Similarity is a prime consideration in wood selection for stack lamination. Wood must be of the same species, same density, same moisture content, same color, same general grain characteristics. Some say that wood used in stack lamination should come from the same tree, but since wood from a single tree may vary widely in inherent characteristics this is no guarantee of compatibility.

Be especially careful to avoid boards that seem lighter or heavier than average. That is an indication of density (and, therefore, hardness) that is greater or lesser than other pieces of wood—a factor that can be troublesome in the finishing stages.

For visual effect, you may wish to mix woods of starkly contrasting colors—maple and black walnut, for example. This is acceptable so long as you fully understand the risks and make allowances for the greater internal stresses that will result.

Fig. 6-3. Hardwood stickered and drying. This wood will have to be kiln dried before it can be safely employed in lamination procedures.

Once the wood is selected, the next step is to test the various boards with a moisture meter. Readings should not exceed 9 percent, and the variation between boards should not be greater than 1 percent.

At the design stage you will have determined lamination thickness. This may vary, although it will seldom exceed two inches [5cm]. But whatever thickness is selected, it will apply to all laminae, unless some peculiar application is involved.

Fig. 6-4. The moisture meter not only indicates maximum allowable moisture content within wood being used in lamination, but it also is used to determine maximum allowable latitude between pieces. Not more than 1 percent variation should be permitted.

Begin board preparation with jointing one surface, then running the boards through the power planer. The final tolerances must be the same for all pieces. Board widths may, of course, vary, but it is of utmost importance at this stage that the faces be exactly parallel.

A word of advice. Do not prepare more boards than you can use in three or four days. It does not take long for wood to warp. Also, surface oxidation can adversely affect the bonding properties of the glue.

Fig. 6-5. Again jointing comes first, the jointer both cleaning the face of the board and providing one flat surface.

Fig. 6-6. The power planer cleans, flattens, and parallels the opposing surface. Parallel surfaces are a particularly critical requirement for stack lamination.

When jointing and planing has been completed, examine your stock for the choicest and most evenly matched pieces and set these aside for the top, or most visual presentation, of the piece. Then stack or "sticker" the wood to insure its stability until used.

PREPARING THE WORKING DRAWING

At least two drawings will be required for most stack laminations: the first, a cross section of the bottommost layer; the second, an elevation from the most characteristic orientation of the piece, ordinarily the front. Because these drawings will serve as measurement referents, they must be drawn precisely to scale. Pencilling onto the elevation the lamination "steps" will show the full board dimensions necessary to complete the contour.

Fig. 6-7. The planned view. Here the base of the table has been sketched as it appears through the tabletop.

Fig. 6-8. An elevation will ordinarily depict the piece from its most characteristic presentation. Laminations are usually rendered on the elevation.

Fig. 6-9. Pencilling "steps" onto the laminations. When referring to the drawing for measurements, the woodworker will get a dimension adequate to the flow of the line.

Add any other considerations that must be taken into account to the rendering now, before work begins, so they will not be overlooked during the construction phase. If, for example, extra projections, or "ears," are required for clamping points, indicate them on the rendering.

THE FIRST LAYER

Stack lamination ordinarily proceeds from the bottom up. Begin by edge-gluing and clamping a sufficient number of edge-jointed boards to accommodate the bottom cross section.

When the glue has set and clamps have been removed, trace the pattern for the bottommost piece on this initial layer and band-saw the resulting form.

Before proceeding with the second layer, remove excess glue from the face of the joined boards and examine the piece for any indication of unevenness. Minute variations, particularly those along the glue line, may be removed with a scraper blade or, more customarily, with a hand plane. This step will be repeated on each layer as the stacking continues.

Fig. 6-10. Boards sufficiently wide to accommodate the pattern are edge-glued. The pattern is traced on the surface in preparation for band-sawing.

Fig. 6-11. Planing across the surface of a lamina, in order to insure a precise match with the succeeding layer.

For this planing operation, I use a highly sharpened blade, ground to an angle of twice the thickness of the blade, and ground flat and square with no burning at the corners to indicate loss of temper, then honed on hard Arkansas stone, wet with lightweight oil, to remove the burr. The result is an edge that is literally razor sharp. I set the blade at a very fine cut—just enough to detect and shave any variation—and I work across the grain, or at a forty-five-degree angle to it.

Once the flatness of the first layer has been insured, you are ready to proceed with the second. The process now takes on added complexity, for boards will be edge- and face-glued simultaneously. Moreover, it is with this layer that the piece begins to be hollowed.

To begin, arrange the boards on the bottom lamination and trace them out from underneath. Refer to the elevation in order to determine the change in form. In general, the more complicated the development of a stacked form, the more desirable it is to have a three-dimensional model. For the moment, let us assume that the development is relatively uncomplicated and can be worked without a model.

Measure the change on the elevation, then transfer it to the boards with a pencilled line.

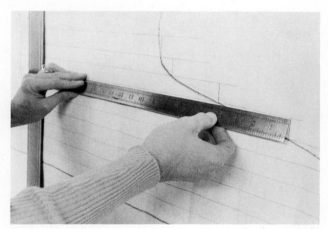

Fig. 6-12. Laminae "steps" must be of sufficient dimension to accommodate surface configurations. When using a scale elevation, one may take measurements directly from the drawing.

Determining the hollowed area of the form comes next. Remember, wall thickness will generally stay within two inches [5cm] unless the form changes drastically. As a visual, rather than structural, consideration you should insure that the vertical glue lines do not coincide with those on the layer below. It is at this point that the importance of utilizing parallel-edged boards becomes evident. Incidentally, center pieces cut out to achieve a hollow form can be reused in subsequent laminations with a perfect edge-to-edge fit. This is economical in terms of wood as well as time.

Before taking the pieces to the band saw, you will find it helpful to employ here a simple system of coding, since wood pieces have a way of getting mixed up, especially if one is turned over inadvertently.

The pieces are then ready to be band-sawed, dusted, and further made ready for gluing.

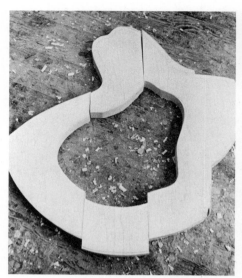

Fig. 6-13. The interior of this lamination has been band-sawed away prior to gluing in order to provide a hollow core.

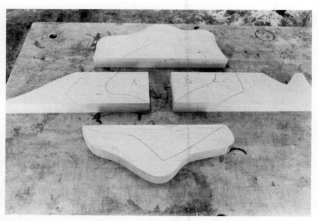

Fig. 6-14. Boards to be used in single lamination. The requirement that each fit perfectly with its mate, despite any interruption, points up the reason why, in the wood preparation phase, exactly paralleled surfaces are provided.

GLUING AND CLAMPING

A wide assortment of clamps will be necessary for this phase of the lamination procedure. As Figure 6–15 and others in this section indicate, there can be no skimping with clamps. I spoke in detail about clamps in Chapter 2, but want to reiterate here that aside from a fifty-ton [45t] veneer press, there is no alternative to clamps. Not metal weights nor rocks nor jack-posts nor the weight of cars, air- or water-filled tubes, nor any other such jerry-built arrangements can provide the force necessary for proper face-gluing.

In stack lamination, edge-gluing does not require quite the exerted force that face-gluing does, and it is possible to utilize "dogs" to hold together edges while glue is drying. These devices, which look rather like oversize staples, have the ability to drive together edges in a tight bond. Care must be taken, however, that the resulting holes do not interfere with the surface that will emerge when the carving is complete.

Fig. 6-15. Face-gluing will require clamps at no less than three inches [7.6cm] on center.

Fig. 6-16. Interspersing dogs with clamps provides lateral pressure for edge-gluing.

A method I find highly practical in bonding edges involves applying clamps at about eighty degrees from the vertical. They will exert not only downward pressure, but (in the process of trying to right themselves) forward pressure as well. I call this the "walking clamp" method. It is a most useful trick of the trade, and it is easily mastered.

Clamps should be positioned as closely together as possible and still allow you convenient grasp on the handle—which is to say, about three inches [5cm] on center. If more clamps are needed (never less!), position them upside down to make the handles accessible.

Fig. 6-17. Lateral pressure may also be applied using the "walking-clamp" method. Applying the clamp at an angle drives the edges together.

For the first two or three layers, you may find it necessary to use large battens, reinforcement boards that insure true flatness between layers by defeating the tendency of boards to develop a cup along the grain. Later, when a number of laminations have been assembled, the form itself will be of sufficient bulk to cope with the problem.

The layering process continues until the form begins a marked change in shape. Let us suppose, for example, we are dealing with a table whose pedestal has a trunklike form. We begin the laminations one on top of the other in a diminishing fashion, as the trunk characteristically grows more slender. But then comes that layer when the form begins to branch out toward the tabletop. Here—or better, a lamination or two beyond this point—it is advisable to stop adding laminae long enough to do some preliminary carving. This is more a matter of prudence than anything else, for at this stage the piece is generally small enough to be maneuvered with ease.

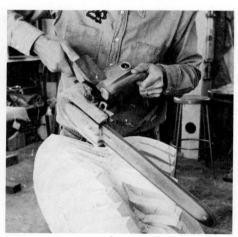

Fig. 6-19. Carving the table base midway through the lamination procedure, at a point when it is still reasonably maneuverable.

Fig. 6-18. In the early stages of stack lamination, a batten may be used to prevent warping.

It is also at this stage, when the form begins to branch outward, that you must be on the lookout for a number of mechanical problems. For example, be concerned with clamp reach. In the design phase, a sudden transition from an upright series of laminations to a much broader one must take into account the limitations of the clamping mechanism. From the point of view of the wood itself, a long, exposed glue line can become a visual problem.

Yet another, rather curious, difficulty that tends to develop at the later stages of stack lamination is *droop*. In an overhanging lamination, the weight of the clamps may cause the board to sag. Any indication that this is in the offing should send you scurrying for your battens.

Affixing the topmost layer presents its own peculiar problems. Each woodworker will tend to develop his own favored method of dealing with them. Some may wish to edge-glue and clamp the entire top before adhering it to its base. It is obvious that such a procedure permits a high degree of accuracy in bonding the edges. Also, it allows for a greater clamp pressure. I prefer to continue as before, edge- and face-gluing in a single step. For the top layer, however, I saw the board in a way that leaves "ears" on which to position horizontal clamps. For vertical clamping, I use pads to protect the surface.

CARVING

Once the lamination procedure is complete, the originally designed form is extracted from the rough layers of wood in a process that proceeds from a chain saw to a #360 grit sandpaper, with a good many steps in between.

I ordinarily begin this work with an electric chain saw, hacking away ears and projections as well as those "steps" that do not approach too closely the finish line. For the undersurface of tabletops I find the power plane particularly useful.

Fig. 6-20. Chain-sawing away the strips on a stack lamination. The carving process invariably begins with a swift removal of large areas of extraneous wood.

The carving becomes more refined with the introduction of a ball mill. This tool is in fact an air-driven die grinder with a one and one quarter-inch [3.2cm] diameter ball mill, four teeth to the inch [2.5cm]. Skill in the use of this implement is a must in the carving of modern lamination forms. Chapter 2 offers a more detailed description of the ball mill and its capabilities.

Fig. 6-21. The air-driven ball mill is the principal carving tool for bringing the wood laminations toward the desired form.

Once the rough outlines of the form have been worked out with power tools, you may wish to introduce hand tools for finer work. A Surform is a particularly helpful instrument in the shaping of flowing lines. Various hand planes—in particular the scrub plane—may also be used during this phase.

Last of all, sand the piece with increasingly finer sandpaper until the surface is perfectly smooth both to the eye and the touch. Apply a suitable finish to complete the work.

STACK LAMINATION USING PLYWOOD

Before leaving this discussion of stack lamination, I would like to mention that with a limited supply of power tools it is possible to fall back upon fine plywoods in the stack lamination technique. The advantages of such a material are immediately apparent: No planing is necessary since parallel surfaces are assured; plywood tends to be an exceedingly stable medium; and the moisture factor hardly enters into consideration.

It is important to remember that not any old plywood will do. The problem with ordinary construction-grade plywood is that it is filled with so many voids and other imperfections that, aside from a practice run or two, it is virtually useless. A much more expensive plywood, such as the birch veneer core type, is what is required. An even finer plywood is Baltic birch, which is imported from Scandinavia and Russia. Die board is the very best plywood available. It is composed of hard maple throughout and contains virtually no interior voids. Unfortunately, it is not only exceedingly expensive, but difficult to find.

The procedure for plywood stack lamination is simple. With a saber or band saw, cut out the layers according to cross-sectional considerations. Then glue and clamp them. The carving strikes through the layers of the plywood at various angles, thus providing any number of interesting visual effects.

Fig. 6-22. Two superior plywoods. The upper is a Baltic birch plywood imported from the Soviet Union; the lower is maple die board.

7.

A Stack Table

The design concept for the stack table came from a whelk shell. The particular shell came to me in a severely eroded condition—the edges had been worn smooth by the action of the sea, the inner chambers were partially exposed. Nevertheless, I found the visual effect most exciting. Revealed was the twisting, ascending structure of the shell. All kinds of philosophical and aesthetic implications might be read into its shape, but for me its power lay in its primitive, organic lines.

By a process of preliminary sketches, I transformed the lines of the shell into the table's essential shape. I gave to the pedestal the shell's sensuous spiral, shading contour lines to lend the illusion of depth. But because the complexity of the shape did not lend itself to two-dimensional drawing, it was not until I had made a clay model that the full possibilities of the furniture form I had imagined were revealed. I constructed this model on a scale of one inch to one foot [2.5 cm:30.5cm].

Fig. 7-1. A clay model of the stack table's base. The unfolding, spiral line that dominates the motif here was derived from a weathered whelk shell.

I began the work of constructing the table simply by tracing the base of the model onto grid paper, then enlarging the pattern to full size.

I selected a 6/4 hard maple, the choice determined largely by the finish. It was in my mind to ebonize this stack table, and that would require a fairly colorless wood like maple.

I prepared the wood in the manner already described: I tested it for moisture level, jointed and planed it.

I then selected sufficient boards to cover the first lamina. I edge-glued and clamped them, and when the glue had set, I laid the cut-out pattern on top of the wood and traced it. I then band-sawed the first layer.

With the second layer, I began to hollow the form. I selected and laid on top of the base layer boards sufficient to cover the form. I then pencilled the pattern from below, and finally removed the boards and turned them upside down.

Having transferred the pattern line to the boards, I referred back to the model and altered the tracing sufficiently to begin the upward spiral of the form. The woodworker who does a great deal of laminating soon develops a facility in reading measurements in these alterations by a simple visual reference to the model. For the novice, however, the more tedious process of measuring with rule and/or calipers will be necessary.

I coded the pieces with a series of quick pencil marks to avoid any subsequent confusion, then band-sawed them. Prior to joining lamina #2 to #1, I gave the base layer a fine planing to insure a good glue contact. I then face- and edge-glued the pieces of the second lamina to the base lamina, using dogs and quick-action clamps.

Fig. 7-2. The base lamina has been
edge-glued, then band-sawed to shape.

Fig. 7-3. Tracing the second layer from below.

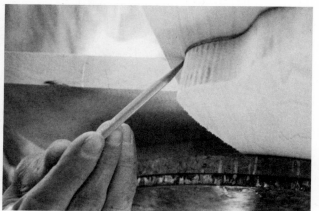

Fig. 7-4. After tracing, I alter the line to
conform to the shape shown on the model.
With second lamination, I begin to hollow
the interior.

Fig. 7-5. The second lamination is both face-glued and
clamped, edge-glued and dogged. At the point shown in the
photograph, only the barest fraction of necessary
quick-action clamps has been applied.

From this point onward, the process of adding laminations proceeded in a similar fashion. I measured and marked changes in form for each lamina. Prior to gluing, I either scraped or planed to perfect flatness the surface of the previous lamina to be fitted. I band-sawed the various pieces of wood involved in each new layer along two lines—the outer being the form line, the inner the hollowing line.

As the stack grew higher, I began to encounter awkward clamp reaches. At the ninth lamination (pictured in fig. 7-7) a deep-throat clamp became necessary. At the fourteenth and fifteenth laminations, other demands began to be made on my stock of clamps. I had to use clamps with sufficiently long shanks to reach all the way to the bottom lamination.

Fig. 7-6. Planing the last lamina applied to insure exact mating for the subsequent one.

Fig. 7-7. Deep-throat clamps provide horizontal reach.

Throughout, I maintained the intervening step of truing the exposed layer to an absolute flatness. Observe in Figure 7-8 that the plane is worked at right angles to the grain. This is but one of a variety of plane orientations worked cross-hatch fashion by which I detected and shaved away the minutest irregularities.

Once the clamps had been secured, I waited at least an hour and a half before adding yet another lamination. There was no need to hurry the process.

Fig. 7-8. After each lamination has been applied and allowed to set, I draw a jack plane across its grain to smooth away irregularities and insure a flat surface for the next lamination.

Like most other woodworkers, I have enough to do without standing around and watching glue set.

At the point where the form had reached its most compact dimensions it began to flow outward toward the top of the table. Note in Figure 7-9 the hollowed area. This helps secure the wood against the dangers of moisture imbalance—and, as a result, splitting.

I halted the lamination process at the seventeenth layer to engage in some rough carving. There were two reasons for doing so at that point. The first had to do with accessibility: The table still lay open to a variety of hand power tools, whereas later the area would become far more restricted. The second had to do with maneuverability: The pedestal was still fairly light and could be turned much more easily than would prove the case before long.

I began carving by knocking off the steps of the laminae with an electric chain saw. This was followed by some basic shaping. I found a bent, flexible slat helpful in providing a controlled arc. I used a felt-tipped pen to outline a spiral contour. I would remind the reader here that felt-tipped pens must be used with care. Ink can penetrate deeply into end grain!

With contour lines indicated, I used an air-driven ball mill for further shaping. For sharper contours, which required another kind of carving implement, I used a pneumatic chisel.

Fig. 7-9. At the seventeenth lamination, as the form of the table begins to sweep outward, I am once more able to secure my clamps to the next underlying layer.

Fig. 7-10. Also at this stage, while the piece is maneuverable, I give the base some preliminary carving. The chain saw rapidly eliminates the steps.

Fig. 7-11. The bend of a slat provides the line for a controlled arc.

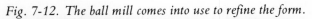

Fig. 7-12. The ball mill comes into use to refine the form.

Fig. 7-13. A pneumatic chisel, driven along the grain line, efficiently removes excess wood and gouges areas requiring sharp relief.

Figure 7-14 shows the form as it neared completion. I had yet to add only a few laminae before installing the top. Note that where the table sweeps outward, much larger laminae are required to overlap glue surfaces. A consequence is the addition of a great deal of weight to this portion of the sculpture, rendering it top-heavy. Accordingly, I carefully hollowed this portion of the pedestal with a gouge to lighten it as much as possible.

Fig. 7-14. As higher laminae are added, I overcome a tendency to top-heaviness in the piece by additional hollowing with gouge and mallet.

Fig. 7-15. Checking flatness of the upper laminae with a straightedge.

As I added the final layers, precision fitting of the laminae became ever more critical. I checked evenness with the help of a straightedge, and with a large jointer plane planed smooth areas out of true. No tolerance for error was permitted in this phase of the construction.

Because of certain visual considerations, I decided in this case to edge-glue the entire top before securing it to the table. Boards were selected, jointed, and clamped together. Following this step, I band-sawed the basic shape of the tabletop. I then secured the last lamina to its base with quick-action clamps. Note here that pads were used to protect the surface.

Fig. 7-16. *The larger surfaces involved in the upper areas of the table require the use of a long jointer plane for smoothing between laminations.*

Fig. 7-17. *In this instance, the tabletop was completely edge-glued and band-sawed to shape before being laminated to the base.*

The first task in the carving stage is the quick removal of a great deal of unnecessary wood. I placed the table upside down on saw horses, then used a combination of chain saw, pneumatic gouge, and power plane to remove the steps and begin the approach to the final line.

I completed the rough carving with ball mill and Surform. Coarse sanding with a body grinder was begun with a #36 grit sandpaper. More sharply contoured areas, however, required the inflatable drum sander. Using the same tools, I kept changing sandpaper toward progressively finer grits: #60, #80, #120, #220. I followed with a final hand sanding using a #220 grit paper. Finally, I applied an ebonized finish.

Fig. 7-18. "Steps" in this configuration are best removed with power plane.

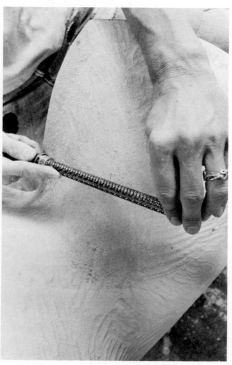

Fig. 7-19. A rattail Surform is the last instrument used in smoothing and refining the form prior to sanding.

Fig. 7-20. Rough-sanding begins with the powerful efficiency of a body grinder. A #36 grit paper is being used here.

Fig. 7-21. Sanding continues through a variety of stages, tools, and grits until the piece receives its final hand-sanding.

*Fig. 7-22. Maple Dining Table (1978):
19 x 50 x 50 in. [73.7 x 127 x 127cm];
stack lamination. Private collection.*

8.

Bricklay and Other Lamination Techniques

In this chapter we turn to other, less common types of lamination procedures: bricklay, scarf, fan, and barrel lamination. None of these techniques is markedly difficult, but each does require basic woodworking skills as well as some engineering and drawing capability. An acquaintance with these variants will provide the woodworker with the necessary versatility to take on a wide variety of forms in ways that are at once aesthetically satisfying and structurally sound. Mastery of these techniques will enable the woodworker to draw upon a wider range of solutions to problems of design, construction feasibility, and stability.

There will be times, for example, when the stacking technique might prove uneconomical or present stress problems that can be resolved only by proceeding with a complementary lamination system. Needless to say, there will also be times when the woodworker will find himself obliged to employ hybrids. A long tapered form, for example, might well begin with stack lamination, move on to the bricklay technique, and end with a bentwood application.

Whatever the requirements of his form, once the woodworker has acquainted himself with the various lamination techniques, he will be aware during the design phase of a full range of procedures suitable to his task. The choice of techniques he makes will be based upon a combination of factors: visual appearance, desired grain arrangement, structural strength, economical wood utilization, and ease of construction.

Fig. 8-1. Burled Elm Coffee Table (1979): 19 x 48 x 16 in. [48.2 x 121.9 x 40.6cm]; bricklay lamination with jointery. Collection Boston Museum of Fine Arts.

BRICKLAY LAMINATION

The term suggests the method. Bricklay lamination utilizes blocks of wood built up rather on the order of a brick wall, with glue taking the place of mortar.

It will be helpful if, from the outset, we distinguish the bricklay technique from bentwood and stack lamination methods. With bentwood, the woodworker uses strips of wood formed along a mold surface, face-glued, and clamped. The technique lends itself to wood forms that are slender and give a sense of suppleness and graceful curvature. With stack lamination, planks of wood are face- and edge-glued to become more substantial forms capable of providing a sense of mass and the appearance of curves along both vertical and horizontal planes. The bricklay method falls almost exactly in the middle of these two procedures. Blocks of wood are face-glued and end- or butt-glued.

Fig. 8-2. Like a rambling brick wall, the base of the elm table begins to take form.

The resulting form is thicker than that associated with the bentwood technique, yet less massive than those produced by stack lamination. According to a somewhat pliable rule of thumb, whenever the thickness of a form exceeds approximately three inches [7.6cm], the woodworker will leave the bentwood method of lamination for that of bricklay. Stack laminated forms less than three inches thick could, conversely, be crafted with the bricklay technique.

Note also that the treatment of the wood grain differs among the three methods. With bentwood the grain flows with the curve. With stack lamination the grain remains constant, as though the form were carved from a single piece of wood. Bricklay, however, results in more abrupt changes of direction in wood grain—indeed, as abrupt as the change in angle of the wood blocks.

Bricklay lamination has not been widely used in furniture production. The essential technique, however, has had a long and valuable career in foundry work; patternmakers often use the bricklay method to form wooden models of gears and other components to be cast in metal.

As applied to sculptured wood forms, the technique has certain advantages, among them the economical use of wood. Such economy is due in part to the scale of the wood used, for the "bricks" are not of any considerable size and can thus be cut out around knots and other imperfections in the stock.

Bricklay also offers considerable structural rigidity. At the minimum three laminae, the form will not possess the tensile strength of bentwood lamination because of the relative weakness of the butt joint. Nevertheless, additional layers quickly add enormous strength; and even three layers, properly jointed and glued, offer far more inherent strength than does a single board of the same size, weight, and type.

Bricklay lamination lends itself particularly well to the construction of hollow forms, especially if they are symmetrical. Asymmetrical arrangements are more difficult with this technique because the "bricks" cannot be cut to a standard pattern.

We should note here that bricklay permits sudden change in the direction within the form. The table base shown in Chapter 9 is an example of this; it shows how the bricklay technique can be used to make an abrupt, ninety-degree change in direction, which, in turn, can be refined into a particularly pleasing flow of wood. This procedure depends upon a technique I call a "stacked finger-joint" (see fig. 8-3). The right angles are accomplished with notched assemblage, the notches not cut, but rather layered together.

Fig. 8-3. A stacked finger-joint enables a bricklay form to change direction abruptly.

In general, the bricklay technique proceeds as follows:

1. Select the lumber and plane it to standard thickness, with faces and edges parallel.

2. Refer to the scale drawing for the length of the brick to be used as well as the butt angle.

3. If the designed piece is symmetrical, all bricks may be cut at the same time to the same measurements. Take special care to cut the ends—which, remember, must be glued also—with utmost precision. For this purpose, I recommend a carbide-tipped blade and a sliding table jig. It is a good idea also, prior to gluing, to fit the pieces on a milled surface to insure that they meet perfectly. Since the butt joint is a potential weak link in the bricklay procedure, it is imperative that the ends meet full and flat. By way of personal precaution, I ordinarily touch the ends to an oscillating belt sander. Properly used, a large disc sander or an ordinary belt sander will serve the purpose nearly as well.

4. Begin assembly on a flat surface, such as a piece of scrap plywood, waxed to prevent glue seizing. (Waxed paper also does very nicely for this purpose.) Referring to your scale drawing, begin the assembly with *layer #2*. Why the second layer? Simply because dogs can then be used to clamp the butt joints together without marring the visible surface. The resulting holes would be visible on the first layer and, therefore, unacceptable.

Fig. 8-4. *When preparing the "bricks" for lamination, touch the ends to an oscillating belt sander to insure true mating of ends.*

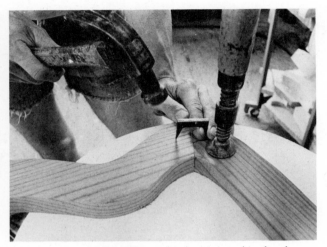

Fig. 8-5. *Dogs will pinch together butt joints, but they leave holes in the wood surface.*

5. Prior to applying the glue, prime the butt ends. End grain is highly porous, and glue can be forced into the pores under pressure in such a way that the bonding will be marginal. Priming can be accomplished either by applying a layer of glue and then wiping it off, or, for a faster priming, using a diluted hot glue. Once primed, give the butt ends of layer #2 a final coat of glue and dog them tight.

6. When this second layer (the first assembled) has set, be careful not to disturb the form. My rule is to leave the laminated form exactly where glued and proceed with the next layer, usually #3. (If the form lies reversed on the plywood, the next layer will, of course, be #1.) Like a mason positioning bricks on a wall, stagger the joints so that the middle of one block corresponds with the glue line of the block below it.

7. Apply glue to both the face and the butt (having first primed the butt). Quick action clamps provide vertical pressure. With mid-layers, continue to use dogs to provide horizontal clamping pressure. With the top and bottom layers, however, replace dogs either with a walking clamp technique (see page 97) or horizontal clamps attached to ears.

Fig. 8-6. The porous character of the butt ends requires that they be primed before final gluing.

Fig. 8-7. Bricklay laminations simultaneously dogged and clamped.

SCARF LAMINATION

Scarf is an old Scandinavian term that refers to the joining of wood by a process of notching and cutting on the diagonal. A procedure of considerable antiquity, it was originally used to lengthen boards. As applied to modern lamination technique, however, the scarf joint has taken on some ingenious variations. Its primary virtue lies with the fact that it eliminates butt gluing and allows for a stronger glue joint along the bias. At the same time it provides an all-but-invisible joint, which permits the wood grain to maintain a linear flow. Scarfing is also useful in working up curves along a three-dimensional plane. If the scarf joint is twisted out of plane, the curve can take off in a new direction. Figures 10-4 and 10-20, in Chapter 10, show finished pieces in which scarf lamination was employed in combination with other techniques.

In the technique described below, dowelling replaces notching. Otherwise the technique remains similar to that used on Norse ships during the Iron Age, when bow planking was lengthened through a process of scarfing.

The general procedure for scarf lamination is as follows:

1. Begin by planning the joints on the scale drawing to allow for a minimum interruption of the grain flow. In the piece illustrated in Figure 8-8, a single vertical layer is involved. Additional layers can be built up in bricklay fashion. Whatever the complexity, plan as long a joint as possible. This permits increased strength through a longer gluing surface.

2. Cut the scarf joints on either a variety saw or a band saw, depending on convenience and on the vertical dimension of the piece. Precision is not a critical factor at this stage, inasmuch as the joint will be either run through the jointer or hand-planed prior to gluing.

3. Dowelling follows. The purpose of the dowel is to prevent the scarf joint from slipping when clamp pressure is applied. By way of a bonus, it will give additional strength to the glue surface. Accordingly, drill a dowel hole somewhere near the center of the joint to a depth of approximately one-half inch [1.3cm]. Dowel size will vary according to the size of the scarfed pieces, with a median in the area of one-half to three-eighths inch [1.3cm– .9cm]. Use a dowel centering device to mark the opposing hole, then drill it out to a corresponding depth.

Fig. 8-8. Scarf jointery to achieve a curved grain flow. Note that the scarf joints, even in rough form, are almost invisible.

Fig. 8-9. Doweling the scarf joint insures that it will not slip out of position during the clamping process.

4. Before gluing, dry-fit the scarf laminae to insure that the joints match perfectly and the dowels line up.

5. Begin gluing by inspecting the end grain. If a considerable amount shows, prime the joint in the manner described for bricklay lamination (page 116). Then apply the final coat of glue, making sure to cover dowels and dowel holes as well as the joint surface.

6. Clamp the joints as tightly as possible. Because the pressure of the clamps will tend to raise the fine point of the angle, additional clamping will be needed here. By way of checking the pressure of the clamps on the glue surface, I inspect the joint by slicing into it with a chisel. I can quickly ascertain by this method that I have a perfect fit.

Fig. 8-10. Slicing into a clamped joint to insure accuracy of fit.

FAN LAMINATION

As the name implies, fan lamination utilizes wood sections that are wedge- or pie-shaped along the face to create a circular or arched form. The wood is sawn so that the grain radiates from the center; the resulting sunburst effect is visually quite pleasing.

Tabletops can be made employing fan lamination, although stress factors do not permit the circle to be completed. If you want a fully circular top with a fan effect, you will have to resort to a veneering process. The backs of chairs, bar tops, and the like can also be made by a fan lamination process. All the same, the applications of the procedure tend to be limited by several factors, not least of which is an undue number of construction problems, especially those associated with clamping arrangements. These must be worked through during the design phase, or else you may find yourself come to grief midway through the project.

In general, the process follows these steps:

1. In the design phase, avoid becoming so excited over the various visual possibilities presented by fan lamination that you overlook the technical difficulties, especially those involved in bonding angled surfaces. Wedge-shaped pieces of wood, for example, narrowed to a fine point cannot with-stand clamp pressure. In fact, the width of the narrowest end should not be brought much under one half inch [1.3cm]. Similarly, the outward radiating angles should not be too extreme or clamping problems will ensue. A wide angle further exposes an overabundance of end grain, which will present insurmountable gluing difficulties. About three inches [7.6cm] at the wide end should serve as a maximum width for the design—although this, quite naturally, depends on the scale of the fan.

2. The band saw is the most convenient means for cutting fan laminae. The edges will be jointed later, so precision is not an overwhelming considera-tion during the sawing process. If, however, you have planned a perfectly symmetrical form, with all laminated pieces of the same dimensions, then the variety saw can be coupled with a taper jig, and all pieces cut at the same time. Mark boards so that two pieces can be sawn vertically from a single length, with a diagonal cut along the center. Do not worry about the small variations in grain direction. Since the bias is slight, and because grain tends to wander in any event, the procedure will not be detectable in the finished product.

3. Joint edges of the laminated pieces. Take all necessary precautions while using a power jointer with wood of these proportions, and use a pusher to guide the stock over the blades.

4. In preparing to glue the edges of the laminae, you will want to use at least one dowel to prevent slippage. If maintaining a flat face is critical, use two dowels. Drill holes and locate opposing holes accurately. Finally, apply the glue.

Fig. 8-11. Dowels also keep fan laminae from slipping.

5. For clamping, the jig shown in Figure 8–13 can be fashioned from scrap wood and used for securing the foot of the clamp. The steps of the jig keep the clamps at right angles to the glue line. Wooden pads protect the opposite edge from being marred by the jaws of the clamp. Remember, it is important to protect all jointed edges!

Fig. 8-12. An inexpensive dowel-centering kit enables you to locate the opposite dowel hole and to drill it precisely.

Fig. 8-13. A clamping jig prevents clamps from slipping along the fan laminae.

6. Fan laminations are best handled if pieces are glued in series of twos, with a third (and possibly a fourth) lamina added to the initial pair. As the clamping angle increases, the jaw of the clamp will have a tendency to ride along the edge. This can be avoided sometimes by folding a piece of sandpaper in thirds and placing it between clamp and wood. The sandpaper takes the place of the wooden pads and grips the edge more securely.

7. With a number of sections consisting of three or four laminae already glued together, begin the final clamping procedure. Many options are open, none of which is entirely foolproof.

a. First, if the wedges are not much over thirty inches [76.2cm] long, they can be end-clamped together with dogs and what is called a "reverse spring joint." This is a jointing procedure in which the edges of the board are given a slightly convex shape (in the thousandths of an inch) so that, as the dogs pinch the boards together, pressure is equalized along the length of the board. This technique requires that the wedges be longer than the finished length so that the wood at the ends damaged by the dogs can be sawn away after the glue has set. In general, the procedure is fraught with risks, not least of which is the possibility of splitting the wood with the dogs.

Fig. 8-14. Small pieces of sandpaper folded in thirds also keep clamps from creeping along an angled surface.

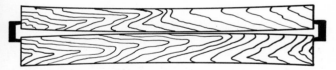

Fig. 8-15. In the "reverse-spring" joint, the edges of the laminae are shaved a few thousandths of an inch extra at the ends, giving a slight bow to the surface to be joined. Dogs driven at both ends equalize pressure along the length of the boards. The convexity has been exaggerated here for purposes of clarity.

b. A second, and more prudent, method involves clamping blocks that are glued to the faces of the wedges. Such blocks should be cut from a wood softer than that used in the form so that they can be broken clean after the gluing is completed. The residue can then be planed away easily. Once the glue has been applied, engage old-fashioned hand-screw clamps on the clamping blocks. This type of clamp performs better because of handle placement.

Use a minimum of four such clamps and tighten them alternately to avoid any undue stress at one point or another. The correct pressure will always be half guess and half gamble. The clamp must not be applied too loosely, but overtightening risks breaking a clamping block. Watch the glue flowing out of the joint to determine evenness of applied force. More important, slice into the joint with a chisel to determine the quality of the fit. After the glue has set, break off the clamping blocks with a chisel and plane the surface smooth.

Fig. 8-16. Checking the glued joint of a fan lamination by slicing into it with a chisel.

I should point out that it is possible to saw ears into the wide end of fan laminations. This means that those tricky clamping blocks need be used only at the narrower end.

BARREL LAMINATION

Barrel lamination is a variant of traditional cooperage. The difference is that, whereas in the customary manufacture of barrels and casks staves are steam-bent in advance, then formed and harnessed with metal hoops, in barrel lamination all curvature is accomplished by sawing, rather than steam bending, and the completion of the process depends on edge-gluing, not banding.

Any form that has a long, thin, circular shape is suitable for barrel lamination. The technique permits economy of wood utilization. The resulting form tends to be lighter than that provided by other lamination procedures, and the face presents a pleasing vertical flow of the wood grain. Figure 10-19 shows a piece made by barrel lamination.

The steps in barrel lamination proceed as follows:

1. Calculate the edge angle by referring to a top view of the scale drawing. Although a symmetrical form is easiest to saw, there is no great difficulty in working out a variety of angles for a more varied form.

Fig. 8-17. Measuring the angle of a bevel for a barrel lamination.

2. To prepare the glue surfaces, set the angle on the variety saw to cut at the pitch required by your design. Adjust the tilt fence on the jointer accordingly. Then saw and joint the pieces. Once again, dowels are used to secure the bonding of the edges and to align the members. In drilling dowel holes, it is important to keep away from any proposed carving areas.

3. As was the case with fan lamination, bonding the first few barrel laminae is relatively easy. As the form progresses, however, the difficulty of applying pressure to glue joints increases. The easiest procedure involves a completed circle of laminated pieces in which band clamps provide the pressure.

4. If only a partial circle is involved, you will be forced to use one of the clamping techniques described above in the section on fan lamination: Dogs may be used in conjunction with a reverse spring joint, or clamping blocks may be glued to the laminae faces.

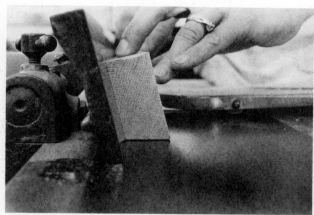

Fig. 8-18. *In jointing the angle for a barrel lamination, tilt the fence of the jointer to the appropriate degree.*

Fig. 8-19. *Applying glue to barrel laminae.*

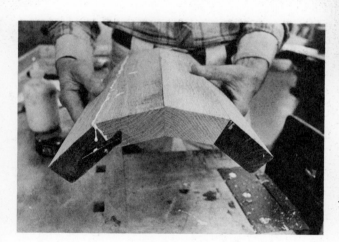

Fig. 8-20. *Barrel laminae may be clamped with pinch dogs, using a reverse-spring joint technique.*

Bricklay, scarf, fan, and barrel lamination techniques will be used less often than bentwood and stack procedures. They do nonetheless provide a necessary versatility for the woodworker who begins to take on more complex forms. The serious craftsman will want to master these techniques.

9.

A Bricklay Coffee Table

Much of a woodworker's creative potential lies with his ability to play with design concepts. A playful approach involves humor and, with it, the capacity to bring together seemingly impossible opposites.

Much of my design work attempts to reconcile a variety of forms that may, at first thought, seem incompatible. I try to carry out this mating of improbables in a light-hearted manner. There is little need to point out the futility of those grim strivings for novel expression that mark so much of twentieth-century art. Most of these efforts end merely with boredom. But when whimsy and fancy enter the situation, as in the music of Eric Satie or the art of Marc Chagall, the listener or viewer is far more apt to react with surprise or delight.

The idea, for example, of a chunk of glass being supported by a rubber bandlike form seems ludicrous enough. Glass is hard, brittle, fragile. A rubber band, on the other hand, is floppy, soft, elastic. Yet these contrary notions can be brought together. The flowing propensities of wood, especially when subjected to the shifts in plane made possible by the bricklay lamination technique, can be made to approximate the eye-pleasing shape of a flat rubber band twisted and left coiled and collapsed.

The idea intrigued me. I toyed with the form, modified it, reoriented it. By restructuring the loop, I gave the rubber band the look of a Möbius strip, that fascinating phenomenon of the continuous surface which defies visual logic. I played some more with the emerging design, purposely distorting it, refining and modulating it until, at last, a coffee table emerged—a coffee table that has for its surface a thick slab of plate glass supported beneath by a flowing loop of wood.

My first effort with this design idea was undertaken a number of years ago. The basic concept came easily: glass and, highly visible under it and through it, a sculptured wooden skein. I knew that by utilizing the bricklay lamination technique it would not be impossible to create the form I wanted, but as early as the design phase I could see that the work would be exceptionally tedious. Since the form was without an essential symmetry, each angle, each "brick," each size, each joint would have to be calculated and processed differently. The construction thus would move slowly, as the form was built up wooden brick by wooden brick.

In the end that was how it turned out. The construction seemed endless. I soon found myself left with the sort of project dreaded by woodworkers in which the recompense for their labors drops well under the minimum wage.

Fig. 9-1. Rosewood and Glass Coffee Table (1977): 19 x 36 x 48 in. [48.3 x 91.4 x 121.9cm] (glass 48 x 60 in. /121.9 x 165.1cm); bricklay lamination with jointery. Private collection.

For all that, the eventual result was so pleasing that I immediately set about attempting a similar construction, but one using a much simplified building procedure. It took many hours at the design table, but eventually I came up with the idea of a bricklay procedure that would result in two sets of four identical laminated pieces. When finished, I would join the eight pieces into a rough, looplike form by means of spline joints. Then, in the carving stage, I would give the sculpture its random, asymmetrical shape with ball mill and rasp.

Once I had settled on this mode of construction, I returned again to the basic design. A random loop based on a Möbius strip can be drawn on paper without any great difficulty, but there is no way of gaining the necessary variety of perspectives without endless sketching. The more practical approach, therefore, is to make a model.

Although there is a standard armature for this type of model that can be purchased in an art supply store, it so happened that I did not have any lying around the shop at the time. Nor was I in the mood to drive to Rochester to find one. As it turned out, there were some leftover electrical supplies lying around. I stripped the insulation from some #10 copper wire and, using it as the armature, began working out the basic lines of the loop until I was satisfied. Next, I applied clay so that I could solve the problems of the continuous surface.

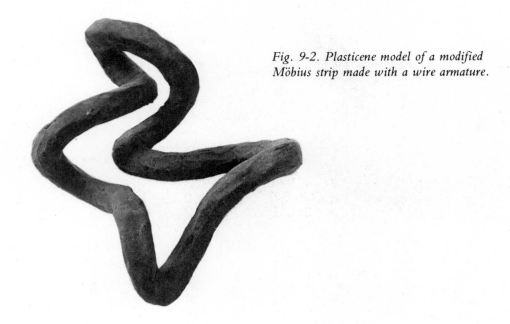

Fig. 9-2. Plasticene model of a modified Möbius strip made with a wire armature.

With the model completed to my satisfaction, I began the scale drawings. Here once more the construction problems had to be anticipated in advance. It was not enough to make a scale rendering of the finished form. Rather, it was necessary to proceed mentally through every step in the process, including such practical considerations as the location of clamping points in the final assembly.

When at last the time came to begin construction, I chose from my woodshed several pieces of 6/4 cherry. I dimensioned the lumber on the jointer and power planed it to a thickness of approximately $1^{5}/_{16}$ inches [3.3cm].

According to my scale drawing, a total of sixty-four bricks were required for the project. Only two angles were needed—forty-five and ninety degrees—but there would be five different brick sizes, meaning that the variety saw would have five different adjustments.

When cutting bricks for a loop, it is of some importance to keep the angles accurate; otherwise, the woodworker may find that he is unable to complete the loop. For this type of precision sawing, and for quickly duplicating bricks that must be interchangeable, I've developed a sliding table jig for use with my variety saw. It not only provides a great deal of accuracy, but also turns out bricks at a rapid rate. The sixty-four bricks were cut in no time at all, and stacked in five separate piles.

At this point I primed the joints for gluing in the manner described in the previous chapter.

Assembly followed. I began with the middle layer. First I clamped a center brick to a waxed Formica surface used especially for this purpose. I applied a second coating of glue to the butt ends. I then hammered dogs into the brick faces to pinch together the three elements of the form. I applied more quick-action clamps vertically to insure that the three joined bricks were lying perfectly flat.

Fig. 9-3. Dogging the middle layer of what will be a triple-stack bricklay lamination.

When the glue had set, I removed dogs and clamps. Since the bricks were held together by glued butt ends alone, I was careful to leave this layer undisturbed on the Formica. With the form in place, I carefully scraped glue and wood irregularities to insure a true matching surface for the next layer.

There followed the application of one of the outside layers. Placement of the first brick here was critical. Before applying glue, I positioned the element just so and marked it along the center line. I then coated both the joining faces and butt ends of the bricks with glue and clamped the layer into place. Since this would be one of the surface laminae, I could not use dogs. Instead, I applied clamps at an angle that exerted pressure on both face and butt end—what I have referred to as the "walking-clamp" technique.

Once the glue in this layer had set, there was no further need to deal gently with the form. With two layers, a bricklay lamination becomes incredibly rigid. I turned over the form, scraped it, and applied the final layer in a manner identical to that used on the opposite side.

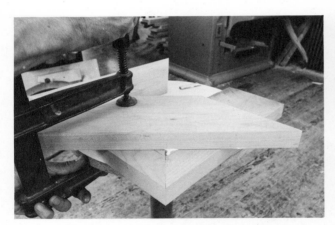

Fig. 9-4. Positioning the first brick of one of the outer layers.

Fig. 9-5. The second brick, its butt end having been primed and given its second coating of glue, is added next.

Fig. 9-6. With outer layers, I use a "walking-clamp" technique to provide lateral clamping force.

I repeated the procedure—a most simple one—seven times. Half of the forms were proportionately smaller than the other half, but the lamination technique was virtually identical.

When I had completed all laminated forms, I took the various sections to the band saw and cut them to shape.

Figure 9-8 shows the sections laid out and ready for the final stages of assembly. The various parts have an elementary look about them. In fact, they are elementary—far more so than the forms involved in the first table I made along the same lines. But this simplicity came at the price of a great deal of frustration, as well as many hours of problem-solving at the design stage.

The next step involved the truing of the butt joints. Since these had been cut on the band saw, it was necessary to refine the angle. I carried out this task on the oscillating belt sander. I realize that many readers may doubt that it is possible to achieve such exact tolerances with a belt sander. But if both ends of the form are sandwiched and simultaneously sanded, you can be sure that they will meet perfectly.

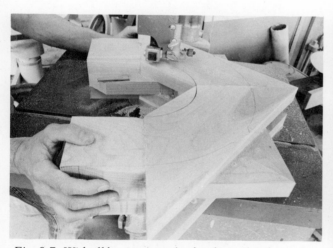

Fig. 9-7. With all laminations glued and set, I band-saw the designated form of the piece.

Fig. 9-8. The bricklay forms of my ribbon table together with the splines by which they will be joined. When fitted together, they will be carved in such a way as to provide the effect of a Möbius strip. Note the ears, which have been left on the forms to serve as clamping points.

Once I had completed this process, I cut spline joints. Ordinarily, this type of procedure is performed with a dado blade on the variety saw. However, we have the good fortune to own a Bridgeport vertical milling machine, which can be equipped with a half-inch [1.3cm] router blade and do the same work a little more quickly and precisely.

Fig. 9-9. A Bridgeport milling machine is used to rout the spline joints.

For the splines I was obliged to adopt the trial-and-error method. The sort of tolerances involved with splines can be extremely difficult to measure—the procedure is more an art than a science. Splines must fit exactly, but not too tightly; that might spell trouble when the glue has been applied and one is left no way of maneuvering the forms. And so, I planed pieces of scrap cherry again and again until they fit the joints to perfection. Then I cut these splines to length on the variety saw.

Before final assembly, I dry-fitted the eight pieces to insure that all elements would come together easily and exactly, then I lettered the parts to save time later on.

I began assembly by pairing forms and gluing two at a time. Figure 9-11 shows how nicely the bricklay technique lends itself to an abrupt change in the plane of lamination. The transition from a horizontal to a vertical plane is actually accomplished through spline joints.

Fig. 9-10. As uncomplicated as any laminated assembly may appear, it is always best to code the parts prior to gluing.

Fig. 9-11. Gluing proceeds by pairing components and working from smaller to larger forms.

After this first series of joinings, four larger pieces remained. These again I paired and glued, leaving two pieces.

Before gluing the last two spline joints, I dry-fitted the pieces for the last time. Gluing two joints at the same time can be tricky—no sense in tempting fate at this stage of the construction!

Fig. 9-12. The bricklay form is splined and glued. The twist causes apparent misalignments at the spline joint. This will all be carved smoothly away.

I began the work of shaping the piece by removing the clamping ears with an ordinary cross-cut hand saw. Neither at this point nor during any other phase of the carving process did I pick up the chain saw. The reason is that with certain bricklay applications come sudden shifts in grain flow and with those shifts comes the danger of chip-out, especially when a roughing tool like the electric chain saw is used. So, once I had removed the clamping ears, I did all of the carving with a ball mill, and relied upon rasps and Surforms for refinement.

Fig. 9-13. The carving process begins with the sawing away of the clamping "ears" with a hand saw.

I was helped in the work of shaping by pencil lines and frequent referral to the model. With a Möbius strip, one must begin at one point on the form, then work gradually around it to complete the spiral.

Fig. 9-14. Again the ball mill serves as the primary instrument of carving.

Fig. 9-15. A Surform serves to smooth the wood and bring the form to shape.

I followed with sanding, then applied a standard oil finish, and completed the piece by fitting it with a custom-cut square of three-quarter-inch [1.9cm] plate glass.

Fig. 9-16. Giving the piece a final hand-sanding.

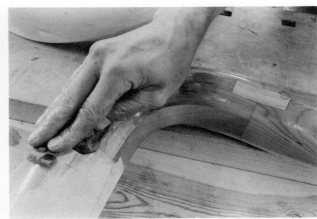

Fig. 9-17. An oil finish completes the work.

Fig. 9-18. Cherry and Glass Coffee Table (1979): 19 x 35 x 35 in. [48.3 x 88.9 x 88.9cm] (glass 42 x 42 in./106.6 x 106.6cm); bricklay lamination with jointery. Private collection.

10.

Portfolio

The following portfolio of photographs was chosen to display the versatility inherent in the lamination techniques described in this book.

In order to demonstrate the adaptive character of various methods of wood lamination, I have chosen somewhat more complicated forms than I might have otherwise preferred, most notably with regard to those requiring a commingling of techniques.

Do keep in mind, however, that simplicity both of line and construction will benefit as much from lamination technology as will highly intricate structures.

The various pieces are grouped according to the type of lamination procedure involved in their construction.

Fig. 10-1. Adjustable Cherry Piano Stool (1963): 18 x 24 x 14 in. [45.7 x 61 x 35.6cm]; stack lamination. Private collection.

Fig. 10-2. Cherry Table and Chair Mounted to Floor (1964): 30 x 56 x 36 in. [76.2 x 142.2 x 91.4cm]; stack lamination. Collection of the artist.

Fig. 10-3. Cherry Settee (1968): 30 x 76 x 38 in. [76.2 x 193 x 96.5cm]; stack lamination. Private collection.

Fig. 10-4. Walnut Dining Table (1970): 29 x 70 x 50 in. [73.7 x 177.8 x 127cm]; stack lamination. Private collection.

Fig. 10-5. Cherry Settee (1973): 33 x 60 x 36 in. [81.3 x 165.1 x 91.4cm]; stack lamination. Private collection.

Fig. 10-6. Cherry Settee (1973): 33 x 60 x 36 in. [83.8 x 152.4 x 91.4cm]; stack lamination. Collection Metropolitan Museum of Art, New York.

Fig. 10-7. Walnut Desk (1973): 29 x 75 x 32 in. [73.7 x 190.5 x 81.3cm]; stack lamination. Collection of the artist.

Fig. 10-8. Walnut Coffee Table with Glass Top (1975): 18 x 48 x 56 in. [45.7 x 121.9 x 142.2cm]; stack lamination. Private collection.

Fig. 10-9. Cherry Coffee Table (1976): 18 x 40 x 48 in. [45.7 x 101.6 x 121.9cm]; stack lamination. Private collection.

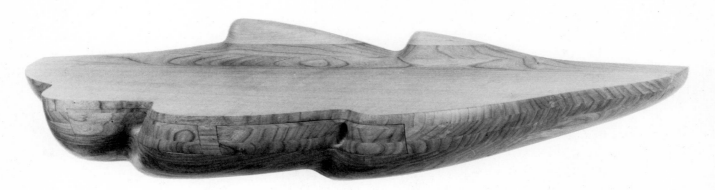

Fig. 10-10. Cherry Wall Shelf with Two Drawers (1977): 16 x 18 x 60 in. [40.6 x 45.7 x 152.4cm]; stack lamination. Private collection.

Fig. 10-11. Maple Desk (1979): 30 x 38 x 70 in. [76.1 x 96.5 x 177.8cm]; stack lamination. Private collection.

Fig. 10-12. Oak and Walnut Chest of Drawers (1962): 48 x 60 x 20 in. [121.9 x 152.4 x 50.8cm]; bentwood lamination and stacked jointery. Collection Museum of Modern Art, New York. (Photo by Peter P. Klose)

Fig. 10-13. Cherry Chaise Longue (1965): 30 x 36 x 65 in. [76.2 x 91.4 x 165.1cm]; bentwood and stacked lamination scarf-jointed together. Private collection.

Fig. 10-14. Walnut Music Rack (1973):
50 x 24 x 24 in. [127 x 61 x 61cm];
bentwood and stacked lamination.
Collection Philadelphia Museum of Art.

Fig. 10-15. Walnut and Leather Armchair with Swivel and Casters (1973): 29 x 27 x 27 in. [73.7 x 68.6 x 68.6cm]; stacked jointery. Private collection.

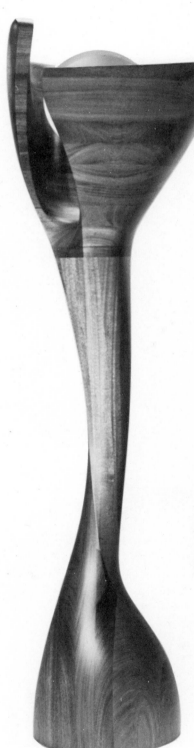

Fig. 10-16. Mahogany Floor Lamp (1968): 70 x 24 x 25 in. [177.8 x 61 x 63.5cm]; vertical and horizontal stack lamination with jointery. Private collection.

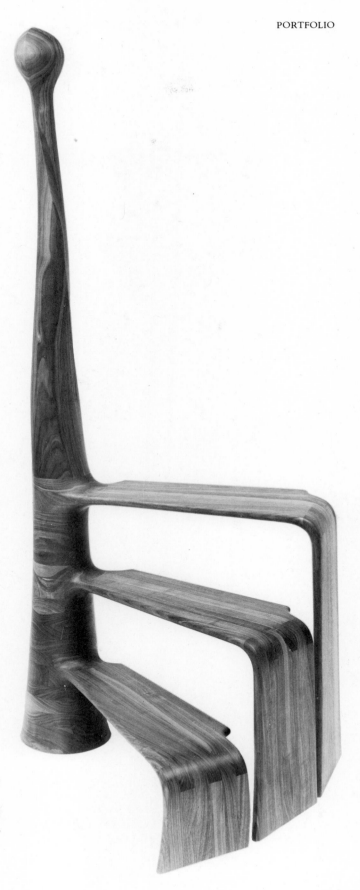

*Fig. 10-17. Walnut Library Steps (1975):
76 x 30 x 29 in. [193 x 76.2 x 73.7cm];
horizontal stack lamination, vertical stack
lamination, and stacked finger lamination.
Private collection.*

Fig. 10-18. Brazilian Rosewood Blanket Chest (1963): 26 x 22 x 48 in. [66 x 55.9 x 121.9cm]; barrel laminated lid. Private collection.

Fig. 10-19. Mahogany Desk with Silver Leaf Top (1965): 36 x 48 x 96 in. [91.4 x 121.9 x 243.8cm]; stack lamination, stacked finger jointery, and scarf lamination. Collection Johnson Wax Co., Racine, WI.

Fig. 10-20. Walnut Staircase (1977): 25 x 9 x 18 ft. [7.6 x 2.7 x 5.5m]; stack lamination with jointery. Collection Gannett Corporation, Rochester, NY. (Photo by Ted Kawalerski)

Fig. 10-21. Walnut Reception Desk (1977): 40 x 38 x 79 in. [101.6 x 96.5 x 200.7cm]; stack lamination. Gannett Corporation (Photo by Ted Kawalerski)

Index